The Limitations of Enlightenment Science

Woody Wood

Devolve!

Leicester, England

Published by *Devolve!*
13 Biddulph Street
Leicester
England
LE2 1BH

Enlightenment Science / Woody Wood — 1st ed.

ISBN 978-0-9931126-3-8

Cover design and Typography by Falcon Oast Graphic Art Ltd.

Printed and bound by imprintdigital.com

Other publications by *Devolve!* in this series: -

Values for Our Time   ISBN 978-0-9931126-0-7

Which Values?   ISBN 978-0-9931126-1-4

A Journey into A Future   ISBN 978-0-9931126-2-1

All distributed by Central Books Ltd.

www.centralbooks.com   44 (0)20 8525 8800

To the philosopher John Gray

— whose insights in

Enlightenment's Wake

set some of us on journeys of discovery.

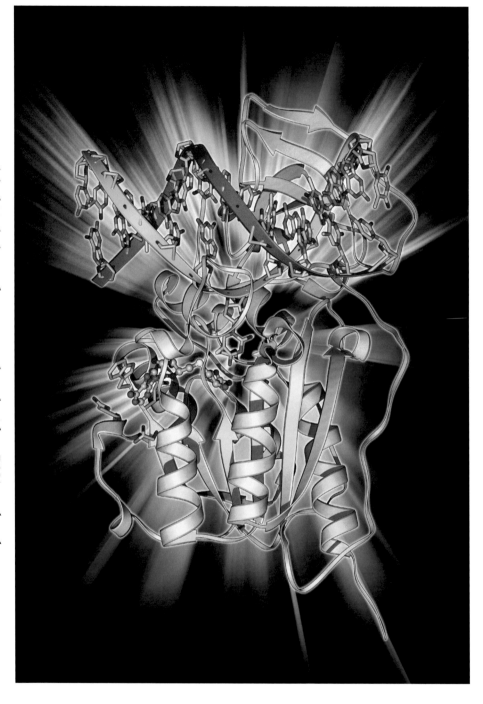

Model of Methyltransferase complexed with a DNA molecule

PROLOGUE

To most of the growing number of people concerned about the threats to life-supporting networks on this planet the problem of human impact* is seen in physical terms. Some few of us are looking deeper: at the world view and values of modern humans – how we got to this place. It will be argued that one of the cornerstones of the values that bear down on us is what i am defining as enlightenment science.

* The term *impact* is here used deliberately to go beyond debates as to whether population or consumption or 'bad technology' is the most critical factor.

ABSTRACT

The early parts of the work can be taken as a journey towards understanding in an attempt to respond to a gathering storm. For myself and others, features of the long struggle between different value systems and world models help to put our present crisis in perspective.

Enlightenment science and its dominant model is examined in the context of this history. It becomes clear that challenges from within and around the model by practitioners with integrity are significant.

Many of these challenges are not merely about 'improving' science. Critically there is an evident intent to go beyond science to metascience – an integrated human wisdom.

Having identified enlightenment science as one of the strands of the ideology of modernity that now threatens our biosphere and therefore ourselves, attention turns to future scenarios, future options and prospects for natural and human life after the impending collision between growth and limits.

*　*　*　*　*　*　*　*　*

THE LIMITATIONS OF ENLIGHTENMENT SCIENCE

It was the age of post-war national service. It was a quiet Sunday in the barrack room. For some reason five of us young squaddies did not have weekend leave passes, nor were we away participating in sporting events.

Just at that time levitation had been in the news and was a subject of general discussion. It had even been featured on television with claimed demonstrations.

At that age i considered myself an atheist, certainly with a materialist view of the world. I was interested in engineering and science and regarded all religious and spiritual beliefs as fantasy.

One of us suggested that we try to do levitation. I thought that this was pointless but went along with the idea as the others thought it would be interesting and there was not much else to do.

The method copied was for one person, 'the subject', to sit on an upright chair while the four others placed their open hands on the subject's head and pressed down hard for about a minute.

Then they quickly placed single fingers under the subject's armpits and behind their knees and tried to lift in unison. (Five of us were the right number.)

Well it didn't work of course, as i knew it wouldn't. The subject's weight didn't change and they experienced some discomfort at the pressure points. Next, someone else volunteered to be the subject and we all did it again with the same result. This seemed to me a very pointless exercise but all the others were up for having a go. After four attempts my scepticism (i didn't have the word then!) was completely justified.

Then my colleagues said: "Let's have a go with you Woody". I couldn't think of a good enough reason to refuse so duly sat on the chair. As the others placed their hands on my head i forgot my disbelief. I forgot everything except resisting the tremendous pressure that felt like it was pushing my head down through my shoulders.

Next moment i was floating up on the ceiling looking down at the shocked faces of my comrades looking up at me. Not sure how long i levitated for but it seemed as if time had stopped. Afterwards i estimated that it was at least as long as a traffic light is on amber, possibly longer. My mind was in a total whirl so i have no clear recollection of coming down except that i certainly did not crash to the floor.

Well, i think that we all wanted to block out the incident. Although some of us remained together for many months we never talked about what happened. As for myself i was sort of aware that my scepticism had ensured that levitation couldn't work but it was to be many years before i could allow myself to grapple with the issues.

* * * * * * * * *

This essay is in part a question mark upon enlightenment science and what i shall refer to as 'the priesthood' that endeavours to maintain its model and methods; to defend itself against heresies – as priesthoods have always done of course.

Now any serious questioning has to look at fundamental assumptions and attitudes. Some of these can be recognised in classical philosophy. I argue that 'errors' (as Plato would call them) go right back to our earliest human and proto-human ancestors becoming aware of the world around them, being troubled by it, attempting to make sense of it.

What follows makes no claim to originality: we all learn from each other all the time. I am especially indebted to critical thinkers who have asked similar questions and attempted answers. Some of them will be referred to (and credited) during the discourse. After a first attempt at an outline narrative a repeat will hopefully fill in some of the gaps.

MODELS OF 'OUT THERE'

Where to start? Maybe with attempts by organic creatures to make sense of their surroundings – and in particular the threats and opportunities that could be presented to them. Since the environment is 'out there' and the creature figuring out how to respond to it is 'in here', even simple creatures will have a *model* of pleasure/pain stimuli and appropriate responses.

This notion that organisms (whether individuals or collectives) have needed to evolve a model of the world in which they are trying to act has many implications in the story of evolution and is arguably the most critical concept for understanding what was to follow.

By the time mammals had evolved this attempt to model the world 'out there' had gone way beyond stimulus and response. A significant biological discovery was the existence of a 'silent area' in the brains of mammals not directly connected to muscular responses. The picture of the environment that the creature (and significantly the group) had to act in became less rigid, allowing optional responses (e.g. fight or flight) and the agony/instability of borderline choices.

As brains continued to grow in size and complexity – partly to cope with intra-group (social) interactions, modelling likewise became more sophisticated. Long before pre-humans were on the scene, such models could represent not only what *is* 'out there' but what *could be*: in other words anticipating the future. For example the hunting strategy of a group of lionesses will take account of the likely escape responses of the prey. Time had arrived in an understanding of the world.

Parietal lobe

Occipital lobe

Frontal lobe

Temporal lobe

I.   Brain Lobes

With the further evolution of large brained proto-humans, experimentation with, and exploration of, the environment could take place partly through mind models. Yet for countless generations these models, if we can call them that, would be direct, 'silent' copies of what was sensed as 'out there'. Likewise any processes leading to action strategies would be what we could best describe as intuitive and were probably experienced in emotional terms.

It appears that there is no agreement among anthropologists as to how far back conceptual thinking and language emerged. Whenever and however this step change in evolution took place it marked a very significant development for our early ancestors. Mind models could achieve a new flexibility less directly linked to the 'out there' that they had originally evolved to mimic.

In the Natural World Story of the essay *Values for Our Time*[1] it was noted that the seventh basic pattern of the Universe that we appear to inhabit may be expressed in the form "every means strives to become an end".

The paradox was that 'creations of the mind' were now apparently free to take their modelling in any random direction yet were acted on by emotional and 'psychological' drives, fears and wishes. The most fantastic belief models could now be created.

OLD AND NEW BRAINS

The insights or Robert Ardrey, the acute observer of animal behaviours and their social group structures, will be referred to later in this essay.

However, in the final chapter of his book *The Social Contract*[2] which was titled The Risen Ape his narrative (dealing with human evolution) becomes more speculative and questionable. In particular he follows Arthur Koestler[3] in asserting that the tragic situation of modern humans arises from our brain structure. The thesis is that the more recently evolved Neocortex ('new brain') is only weakly connected to the more ancient Limbic ('old brain') structures with their emotional and instinctive responses, capacity for aggression, etc.

His argument is that if this old brain can be properly integrated in us moderns then our enlightened rational new brain can lead us to a brighter future, a future in which our creative individuality can triumph over collective 'mediocrity'.

In fairness, understanding of our pre-modern ancestors and their social structures has been developing since *The Social Contract* was published in 1970. Having said that, the ideological bias in favour of an individualism where excellence triumphs is on display. Certainly the opposite case can be made. Our Limbic 'old brains' with their direct interactions with others and with our environments have

II. *Homo Erectus*

12 inches

40 cm

been 'battle tested' over millions of years. In contrast some features of our Neocortex 'new brains' (or more correctly the programmes in them) such as the self-conscious ego ... are arguably at the centre of modern social/political catastrophes and also of much of our personal travails. I plead guilty as charged.

OUR EMERGENCE IN THE PLEISTOCENE EPOCH

Professor Paul Shepard[4] has made significant contributions to our understanding of human pre-history. In *Coming Home To The Pleistocene*, his final book, he presents not only a clear view of pre-human and human social groups in the Pleistocene epoch (approximately 2.6 million to 12,000 years ago) but a strong case that in this mode of existence, *prior* to the development of agriculture and animal husbandry, our forebears were fully immersed in nature and at one with themselves.

Paul Shephard's stance has been critically described as advocating ecological primitivism in contrast to modern civilisation. Now Wikipedia gives the following definition of civilisation[5]: -

"Any complex society characterised by urban development [and] social stratification imposed by a cultural elite [and] symbolic systems of communication [and] perceived separation from and dominion over the natural environment; further defined [among other features] by centralisation, specialisation of labour, domestication of humans and other animals, coupled with ideologies of progress and supremacism."

Leaving aside the question of whether and in what sense 'coming home to the Pleistocene' can have meaning for us today (this issue will be explored in the closing sections of the essay) ... can we really be at ease with ourselves once we understand our roles in this civilisation and its fearful trajectory? Or is this simply 'above our pay grade'; don't we just have to get on with our lives?

THE ROOTS OF ERROR

It will be a core argument of this essay that a series of understandable errors emerged among some early peoples. Also that some of these were carried forward into the age of reflective philosophy and thence, via the scholasticism of a dominant church, into enlightenment science.

Perhaps the most fundamental, most understandable and most tragic fallacy drew on two roots. On the one hand the question: "where did the ancestors go?" – an inability to come to terms with, to accept, the twin miracles of birth and death. At birth a new spirit, a new soul, was considered to come into existence. Yet at death it could not be accepted that this spirit had simply dissolved, ceased to exist, melted back into the Universe. It must have "gone somewhere". Thus the miracle of death, of un-creation, was rejected.

With the development of religious thought "somewhere" was to morph into the elaborate myths of heaven and hell. This rejection of death may yet be the shroud of humanity.

Since 'myth' is often used as a pejorative or put-down label it is important here to defend the term.

A myth is a story, shared among a number of beings to explain an aspect of the world or how things have come to be so. The issue becomes whether a particular myth is helpful or unhelpful; whether it is illuminating, misleading or even culturally fatal.

The second root of the fallacy was the inability of some human societies to fully accept the world they encountered every day, with its mixture of joys and woes, of enchantment and suffering.

In the language of Friedrich Nietzsche[6] they baulked at saying "yes" to life. Their semi-autonomous mind models could allow that behind this "world of appearances" there existed a "real world" more in keeping with their deepest psychological needs.

However, those cleverly constructed 'realities' could not have it entirely their own way. Behind and beneath these conceptual mind models stood – and stand – the much older, more direct, more intuitive and emotional, more 'honest' models of 'out there'.

MODES OF BEING

Now in the Social Story of *Values for Our Time*[7] attention was drawn to the ability (of both groups and individuals) to 'flip' from one mode of being in the world to another when certain triggers were in place. For both earlier peoples and ourselves such triggers can operate the switch from a cool, rational mode to a deeply 'in touch' and emotional mode. These triggers may be operated by personal trauma and tragedy, by certain collective rituals and ceremonies, by mind altering drugs, by some mental conditions and – most commonly – by music that really moves us. (The consequences of facing up to this harsher model of 'out there' could be either a more pessimistic world view or a more courageous stoicism, a determination to say "yes" to our enchanted yet terrible world.)

In *The Birth of Tragedy*[8] Friedrich Nietzsche attempts to address the tension between these two modes of being through the prism of classical Greece. His chosen representatives as both antagonists and complementary forces are Apollo the cool god of form, beauty and illusion and Dionysus the wild god of ecstasy, release and riot.

Apart from personal physical and psychological suffering, Nietzsche had to cope with both an extreme pessimism inherited from Schopenhauer and the burden that the romantic reaction of the nineteenth century placed on art as the redeeming feature of a hopeless world.

Nietzsche's theme was the rise and fall of Greek tragedy. Through its music and its emphasis on the chorus as the embodiment of our deep collective oneness, Greek tragedy, he claimed, was able to put us in touch with that older, deeper, reality.

THE DEATH OF TRAGEDY

It could be said that the counter-challenge by the 'newer' conceptual model of reality with its rational optimism led to the death of tragedy as both an art form and an approach to being in the world. Nietzsche certainly thought so. For him Socrates (who inspired Plato) with his revival of the notion that there was a real world behind the everyday world of appearances and his faith that reason and dialectical argument would solve the problems of the world (caused by ignorance) and would lead to continuous progress ... was the starting point of the false optimism that has led us today to the ideology of modernism[9]. This notion of the 'real world' behind our everyday world was carried over into monotheistic religion as visions of paradise and heavenly eternity.

Christian scholasticism as it evolved in the early middle ages attempted to merge the doctrines of an absolute church with the philosophy of classical Greece. It combined internal doctrinal disputes with ruthless persecution of heretics. Beyond this it was gradually corrupted by its monopoly of thought, its power and wealth. This provoked critical challenges to the church establishment from within.

From this account of the failings of the scholastic church as seen from outside the model and with the advantage of hindsight, it is possible to form a very negative view. This needs to be balanced by a recognition that *within* the model the task of understanding and obeying the will of God was pursued sincerely and diligently by generations of the faithful, both scholars and lay people, in monasteries and in the cycles of daily life.

FROM SCHOLASTICISM TO SCIENCE

With the fragmentation of religious perspectives and an increasingly secular and commercial approach to the world, the pursuit of understanding, both through reasoning and observing, took on the new form of natural philosophy – later to be named as science. Yet the ancient myth that there must be a real world behind this tragic world of appearances, emphatically revived by Socrates, was carried forward into the evolving sciences as the myth of objectivity.

This is not to deny the usefulness of what might be called pragmatic objectivity. If we note certain mountains as a series of pimples on the horizon we can be aware of their distance from us and so understand them as a great mountain range. Yet the concept of objectivity today implies far more than this. It denies the inner, self-experiencing aspect of the Universe and relegates our own self-experience to the merely subjective, with the implication that it is inferior knowledge.

The re-working of the archaic and Socratic myth by enlightenment science can be stated: "behind this world of appearances lies the real world, amenable to scientific method and (often) mathematical formulae – and we, the priesthood, have access to it."

The parallels with scholastic philosophy are quite striking. At the margins of this scientific world view we find sometimes acrimonious disputes over the interpretations and meaning of observations.

At the same time the system closes ranks to defend the model against perceived heresies while remaining in silent denial of theories and observations that cannot be safely incorporated.

To quote from a recent paper by Dr Patrick Curry[10] one of the most perceptive critics of modernity, of which techno-science (his term) is one component: "… institutionally, most lesser-known scientists who insist in giving room to openly metaphoric, system challenging, truth in their work simply aren't hired or published, while middle-ranking ones are ejected from the club as people doing Something Else. e.g. Bateson's version of systems theory; the physicist David Bohm and his 'implicate order'; Stuart Kauffman and complexity theory; Mae Wan Ho's genetics and Francisco Varela's autopoiesis." …

…"Truly eminent scientists such as Einstein, dealing in wisdom, h.dictu., are tolerated in the manner of ex-

Presidents or ex-Secretaries of Defence musing on the contingencies of power, including their own mistakes, in a way that would be completely unacceptable for active players."

One could add to this list the active ex-communication by the priesthood of Rupert Sheldrake, whose ideas will be considered in a broader philosophic context later in this essay.

For the moment we can note that the description of the original edition of his book *A New Science of Life*[11] as "a good candidate for burning" was worthy of the priesthoods of earlier ages.

On top of all this, the distorting effect of funding priorities and the increasing predominance of administration-led rather than academic-led departments finds its counterpart in some of the practices in the latter stages of scholastic dominance.

Once again, this negative picture needs to be balanced by the enormous range of investigation, information sharing and reporting being pursued with integrity *within the model* by countless individual scientists and teams of scientists. It may be said that most of the chronic and acute issues for enlightenment science lie at its own boundaries and its interfaces with new ideas, with the humanities and (most of all) with a very old wisdom.

One of the ways that enlightenment science defends its model against 'heresy' is the strategy of peer review. One road to a more creative and responsive interaction with new wisdoms would be the abolition of peer review. Since that is unlikely to happen – for both good and bad reasons – an alternative might be *dual* review: one critical assessment from within the assumptions of the model, as now; a second one from a very different standpoint such as the humanities or philosophy or a well-known maverick voice.

A BROADER VIEW

In the above descriptions we have tried to trace the evolution of mental models of the world 'out there' with the limited objective of tracing the origins and development of a particular, very significant, fallacy: the myth of the 'real world' behind our everyday reality.

It makes sense now to fill in some of the gaps by revisiting the story of human anthropological and social evolution in a broader context.

As we have just been discovering, our mental models, our world views, have come to exist for their own sake, they have their own autonomy. They can now follow their own fantastic paths – and what a range of 'realities' human imagination can create, driven by our own, often unconscious, desires and fears. At one extreme there is solipsism: the denial that the world 'out there' exists at all. This found its logical counterpart in behavioural psychology which in its fullest expression strove to deny the existence of the human mind!

Now the efforts by our forebears to understand, to make sense of, the patterns of their world and the forces that drove them were linked to efforts to affect those forces. From a modern standpoint it is easy to dismiss the rituals of so-called primitive peoples. Yet this was early science: the attempt to manipulate the world to human advantage. What is more it was accompanied and balanced by humility, awe and wonder – a sense of the sacred. According to Patrick Curry[12] this balanced approach stands in contrast to the 'magic' of techno-science in our age of modernity.

Before again considering the belief systems of traditional peoples, a brief look at the psychological structures that guide human behaviour.

The ninth feature of the *content* of the Universe[13] indicates that a moral issue arises whenever there is a conflict of wills (purposes). In social groups there is an unavoidable tension between the needs of the individual to fulfil its drives and the needs of the group for cohesion, stability and survival. In the Freudian schema this tension is between the Id – a collection of instinctive drives – and the Superego – our internalised social purpose experienced in moral terms.

Back in our evolutionary journey, once humans attained a certain level of awareness – an image of the world that they existed in that included *themselves* – then they would strive to defend this image from any circumstance that threatened or belittled it, that could induce shame or humiliation.

More than this they would act to create circumstances that could flatter and glorify this image. Now this self-image, in Freudian language, is the Ego. The notion of the ego-trip is well understood today.

It was possible to view the situation confronting increasingly aware humans in different ways. They were facing an enchanted world offering stimulating challenges and fearful dangers – on a bad day a terrible world indeed. So our ancestors had a *choice* of how to respond to their world – and the ability to construct their now flexible, quasi autonomous mental models accordingly.

As already noted, the philosopher Friedrich Nietzsche has defined the basic choice (for all of us) as either saying NO to life: "I do not want this vale of tears; I want, I will, another world." … or saying YES to life: "I accept this world with all its beauty and pain, its fulfilments and its tragedies." Nietzsche went on to name his 'yes-sayers' to life as the heroes of his story. Certainly world acceptance, at the cost of pain, could have positive consequences for social groups.

Listing some of these. Enchantment with their world. Stoicism in adversity. Humility before the world; understanding limits. Fulfilment in the cycles of life and work; along with this a cyclic view of time. Knowing beauty in craftsmanship, empathy in social relations and joy in nurturing. Serenity in death. Life as its content; as the journey itself, not any goal.

Yet these amount to a big ask, especially in troubled times. It could be, was, and still is, so tempting to believe – to will – that somewhere there is another better place. Hence the myth of a 'beyond' that we have just been tracing.

If death is a defeat unless there is a beyond, life has to be a journey – in linear time – to get beyond. From our present vantage point of knowing historical practices and glimpsing future possibilities, we can note some of the attempts to get there.

➢ a heaven reached by piety, sacrifice and prayer.

➢ a beyond reached by mummification or cryogenics.

➢ a future of infinite longevity created by the wonders of techno-science.

➢ a realm transfer into a post-organic life.

As the narrative moves forward into historical times the two charts included here attempt a notional timeline of evolving social groups and communities plus the features suggested for them. The first chart [Plate III] presents mainly physical and practical aspects while the second chart [Plate IV] covers social features and beliefs.

Despite drawing on background research both should be treated with much caution: intended to convey the general 'feel' of the social lives of our forebears rather than 'facts'. No dated timeline should be read into the developments since different groups or societies would have reached a particular suggested stage at different times. Further it can be noted that the perspective is largely 'Western' and neglectful of East Asia and the New World.

The earliest human groups were totally embedded in nature so their first interpretation of the forces acting in and on their world was to know them as nature spirits. With the emergence of more complex societies nature spirits evolved into gods supported by various creation myths – still very much within nature.

An account of these belief systems in the cases of ancient Egypt and Mesopotamia was given in *Before Philosophy*[14] Perhaps the most significant aspect of this survey, based on detailed archaeological research, was a revealing exposition of how ancient peoples' understanding of their world, their 'thinking', was so different from our own: with concrete myths in place of our abstract and analytical reasoning.

The narrative also records how the Hebrews – originally a tribe of desert nomads – rejected the gods of a bountiful nature (which had done nothing for them) in favour of a god *beyond* nature, beyond the sensible world. As the authors make clear the Hebrews created a new myth of the will of god – a god who would lead his chosen people to their promised land: provided they obeyed his commandments.

The key transition was not the irony that the god of a 'chosen' tribal people would become the god of two great world religions but that the world was no longer sacred in its own right.

END OF THE PLEISTOCENE

Two other significant social and cultural developments with real consequences for both social relations and belief systems have been the adoption of agriculture and the rise of patriarchy. The emergence of agriculture was fateful for humanity. What it offered was semi-assured food supplies in place of the uncertainties that hunting and foraging necessarily entailed. Yet at what a price.

This price was partly ongoing responsibility and work: tilling the soil, protecting the crops, harvesting, driving off competitors. The archaeological record shows that tribes often reverted to hunting, not convinced that settled agriculture was such a good thing. It also shows the deterioration in body posture and bone structure from the back breaking work[15].

Social Type	Physical Environment	Economy	Internal Economy	Relation with Environment	Tools & Weapons	Land Tenure
Primal Groups (African Genesis)	Jungle/Forest	Foraging + Small Game	Communal	Embedded	Primitive Stone Tools Blowpipes	No Ownership Concept
'Adapted' Groups	Forest + Savanna + Open Terrain	Hunting + Gathering	Communal	Nomadic	Spears Well cut Axes	(ditto)
Pre-agricultural Societies	Various	Hunting/Gathering	Obligations as First Currency	Semi-nomadic	Bows & Arrows Range of Tools Skins; Oil Lamps	Enclosed Encampment
Agriculture based Societies	Mainly Fertile Valleys	Agriculture + Domestic Animals	Tallying/ Accounting	Located	Bronze Tools & Weapons (later iron) Textiles; Sea Power	State Territory (Focused on City)
Judaic Society	Initially: Desert Zone Later: Fertile Land	Initially Marginal Later Agricultural	(as above)	Initially Nomadic Later Located	(not clear)	Promised Land as Territory
Christian/Islamic Societies	Various	Agricultural/ Mercantile/ Pre-industrial	Feudal Obligations to Wage Relations	Located	Evolving Technology	Territorial (fought over)

III.   *Physical Features of Groups*

Social Type	Social Cohesion and/or Control	Belief Systems	Group v Individual Collectivity/Autonomy Interface	View of Time	Social Structure	Language
Primal Groups (African Genesis)	Group Norms; Survival Realities	Embedded Spirits in All things / Fearful yet / Enchanted World	Group Identity predominates	Cyclic	Types/Roles within Cohesive Structure	Signalling Proto-language + Telepathy?
'Adapted' Groups	Group Norms via Shamans	Ancestor Worship / Goddess Worship / Notion of Other World	ditto but Role Identities	ditto	Distinct Roles as proto-classes	Primitive Language?
Pre- agricultural Societies	Group Norms Reinforced by Hierarchies	Local Spirit 'Gods' Origin Myths	Self-Awareness Within Group	Mainly Cyclic	Class/Status roles within bonded whole	Language is Evolving
Agriculture based Societies	Power Hierarchies with Priest Class endorsement	Gods/Goddesses of Sky and Earth / Triumph of Patriarchy	Emergence of Self-Conscious Ego	Cyclic and Linear features	Empires or City States with Control Pyramids / Slaves as 'Others'	Languages + later Writing; Accounting
Judaic Society	Moral Commands + Future Promise	God beyond the World (denial of other Gods) / Anticipated Messiah	Individual Soul Freedom to Sin	Linear: Oriented to Future Home	Priest Led Tribes (former bondage)	Hebraic Language
Christian/Islamic Societies	Permanent Guilt for Original Sin + Promise of Eternal Life	Universal God diverging interpretations	Collective Mode now mainly under threat conditions	Linear: Towards Future World	Initially Feudal: Dual Church and State Hierarchies	mainly Indo-European Languages

IV. Qualities of Groups

Worse than this, because settled agriculture allowed bigger populations and made it feasible to keep captured slaves, the 'we-ness' of the clan was disrupted. New exploited classes were incorporated; forced into continuous work to generate the surplus wealth (stored grain etc.) on which city states with pyramid hierarchies could arise. For most humans working only when you needed to eat was no longer an option. (A deeper critique of the agricultural transition will be offered later.)

Another alleged social revolution was the transition from 'matriarchal' to 'patriarchal' societies. This interpretation of history remains controversial among both scholars and feminists.

To start with the lesser problem, the labels have been considered unhelpful by many and various alternatives have been proposed. Beyond this there remain vigorous disputes about what changes were taking place in the ancient world in the millennia from around 7,000 BCE. Some features do seem to stand out. Possible evidence of Goddess fertility cults is provided by many discoveries of figurines across Europe and beyond, some up to 25,000 years old. There is also fair agreement that before the role of the male in procreation was understood the ability of the female to produce babies was regarded as a reason for veneration. Thirdly, the level of scholarship of investigators such as Merlin Stone[16] supports the core argument that earlier matriarchal or matrilineal societies were progressively overwhelmed by incoming patriarchal cultures; even where specific secondary claims remain open to question.

GREECE, ROME, CHRISTIANITY

The emergence of a Greek civilisation of city states from the dark ages of the first millennium BCE heralded something new in terms of their models of the world around them: their questioning, their 'detached' critical thinking.

I argue now that although they had their own myths of origins with a range of deities and cults there was no overarching god figure to inspire fear and more importantly no controlling priest class to impose uniformity of thought. Whatever, it was an amazing flourishing of culture with recognisably modern ways of looking at the world mixed in with still archaic beliefs in some areas. Philosophy as we know it was being born. An account of this transition can be found in the final section of *Before Philosophy*.

Alas, the ancient option of rejecting the messy, scary world that confronts us was to be carried forward in a new form. Again as previously noted, this was best expressed by Plato, among the foremost of Greek philosophers: behind this world of appearances lies a real world of perfect forms[17]. In the parable of the cave Plato describes us as prisoners trapped in a cave with dim light, seeing shadowy reflections on the walls and taking these to be reality, whereas the 'real' world is in the bright sunlight outside the cave. Aristotle, originally a pupil of Plato, came to reject many ideas of his former tutor. It could be said that Aristotle was much more 'down to earth' or – in terms of this thread – 'in the world'.

After Greece came Rome, eventually the centre of a great empire. Meanwhile, Christianity – originally a messianic sect within Judaism – was opened up to gentiles by Paul and spread across the Roman world. It was initially attractive to women, slaves and the lower classes of society. The appeal of early Christianity was based on two great promises: eternal life after death for individual believers and a reversal of the social order: "the meek shall inherit the earth".

This was characterised by Nietzsche (an unashamed elitist and defender of excellence) as the eventual triumph of *slave morality*, turning our natural life-affirming drives to act in the world, to 'take on' the world, inwards into neurotic forms. (Sigmund Freud acknowledged his debt to Nietzsche.) An example of slave morality today would be the difficulty of liberals with the 'undemocratic' implications of excellence.

Eternal life? This promise, pitched at individuals, carried forward the ancient choice to believe that the 'real' world was somewhere else, beyond and behind this vale of tears. Of course it cheated death. Further, it allowed the existence of the individual soul, with free will to obey or disobey 'the will of God'. This was the tool that the priest class needed to induce guilt for 'sin' and to make everlasting life in heaven conditional on compliant behaviour. With a stroke of genius the notion of original sin was introduced: the people were guilty from birth and now even more dependent on the priesthood for absolution and entry to heaven.

From 320 CE Christianity became the official religion of the Roman Empire and with the subsequent disintegration of that secular power the organised and disciplined Church became a dominant force in the lives of the peoples of Europe and beyond. It was a lean time for free thinking and philosophy for the next few hundred years as the powerful priesthood jealously guarded its orthodoxy. Alternative views, even based on devout interpretations of Christianity, were denounced as heresy and brutally suppressed. Given this reality, the development of thought in response to the challenges posed by social circumstances had to take place within the bounds of orthodoxy. For example, St Augustine and the notion of the just war.

SCHOLASTICISM

As the so-called dark ages in Europe gave way to the middle ages Christian philosophy developed into Scholasticism, already noted as a carrier of the myth of 'beyond'. Apart from such topics as attempted proofs of the existence of God, a critical debate was between *Nominalism* and *Realism*. The nominalists argued that universals were just names for groups or collections of particular things. As an attack on Plato's theory of universal forms (Aristotle's star was rising) this was maybe fair enough.

Unfortunately, the social implication that could be drawn was that groups and communities had no real existence. This was to influence the existential choice to place the human individual rather than the human group or association at the centre of the social world and disrupt the critical balance between collectivity and autonomy. This in turn was another marker on the road to the extreme individualism of the modern world. "There is no such thing as society."[18]

As the Middle Ages progressed the model of the world maintained by Christian orthodoxy was threatened by several factors. First, the increased awareness of national identities coupled with the transition from feudal to mercantile economies impacted on the Church–State dual power balance that formerly held sway.

Second, growing perceptions of corruption eroded popular support for church institutions including the monasteries. Third, and related to this, critical attacks by some scholars began to challenge the establishment from within. John Wycliffe has been described by some as "the morning star of the reformation" – about 150 years before Martin Luther.

PRE-MODERN PHILOSOPHY

The Renaissance had a number of contributory causes but its central feature was a shift in focus from God and salvation to this world and its issues. As is always the case, the weakening of the authority of the central priesthood allowed a new flowering of ideas, of questioning and debate.

The rediscovery of classical Greek thinkers (the last historical period in the West without a single imposed orthodoxy) fed into the ferment of ideas. The invention of the printing press, coupled with rising literacy, enabled new thinking and controversies to reach out more widely across society. In philosophy, the different approaches to understanding for that age soon became clear. Leaving aside the political philosophy of Machiavelli, the dominant strands were *Rationalism*: faith in the reasoning power of the human mind ... and *Empiricism*: studying, measuring, looking for patterns in, the physical world.

Rene Descartes the 'father of modern philosophy' was not only an extreme rationalist who felt that his own mind was the only thing that he could be sure of. He also gave new support to Dualism: the classical belief that the mind and body exist in different realms. In this Descartes has influenced many thinkers even down to the present day.

Although dualism has been challenged by some philosophers and indeed scientists, it was to enable early enlightenment science to 'park' religion as 'something else' while exploring the structure of a mechanical Universe.

Descartes was on safer ground with his rational approach in the realm of mathematics – and the logical principles underpinning its propositions – which appeared to have validity independent of observations. Cartesian co-ordinates became a useful mathematical tool.

While rationalism was dominant across much of Europe, in England (in particular) empiricism, with its emphasis on observation, measurement and pattern recognition, was enabling impressive advances in various branches of what was increasingly labelled as science.

This new science claimed that its *objectivity*: exploring the world as it really was, free from *subjective* perspectives, biases and hidden agendas, was the key to its successes.

It has been argued both above and elsewhere[19] that the concept of objectivity is flawed and that the respect due to those early pioneers is based on their *integrity*.

While rationalism and empiricism were contesting the centre ground of philosophy, other more 'human' approaches were pushed to the margins. Giambattista Vico[20] was way ahead of his time in taking a historical view of social development and change, in which people and their ideas were products of their circumstances. He rejected the idea of a fixed human nature and argued for study of the way that language, myth, law and ritual have interacted in human societies.

SCHOPENHAUER

For our early ancestors the whole world was animated, alive. It was confronted as a thou, not an it[21].

In the next phase of making sense of the world, spirits acting in nature were the driving forces, the mainspring, of the Universe. As early civilizations developed these spirits became the gods of creation, supported in various cultures by elaborate creation myths but still within nature. A decisive break came, as we saw, when the Hebrews dared to place their god outside and above nature. Thus the world was no longer sacred in its own right and the sacred external world lay elsewhere.

Dualism – the separation of mind and matter – enabled the assumption of a 'mechanical' Universe: a dumb Universe operating according to its own intrinsic and observed patterns. (The term 'laws' was now an unfortunate and anachronistic label since the Law Giver had been dispatched to another realm.)

The stunning departure came when the philosopher Arthur Schopenhauer[22] put forward the proposal that the whole Universe – not just you and me – had an inner active side as well as an outer aspect where it (and us) could be observed and described as objects. Schopenhauer didn't have it quite right since his focus on the inside of the Universe (including ourselves) was on its/our active, willing qualities to the neglect of its/our passive, suffering, experience.

None the less this insight solved the dilemma of having to choose between a dumb Universe and one that was guided by some external being. If this picture can be accepted then our earliest forbears had it right after all: the whole world is alive, pregnant with life. The model of a mechanical and *determined* Universe is now under question.

I spoke earlier in defence of *pragmatic objectivity*. This common sense standpoint can be extended more generally to the world around us. Later both a 'quantum' explanation of the limits of objectivity and a broader understanding will be offered.

WHAT IS TRUE?

In contested areas the issue of truth comes to the fore. One of the core aims of enlightenment science was to ensure its monopoly of truth by means of its claim to objectivity. Since the value of that claim has been put under the spotlight on various levels, some of them explored further below, the question of what is true needs to be looked at more broadly.

Without going into the esoteric world of logical propositions there are commonly four main theories of truth, each one with some validity in its own terms: -

The *correspondence* theory of truth asserts that a true statement is one that corresponds with the facts. Since the supposed facts can themselves be the issue in dispute, this definition is arguably the shallowest.

The *coherence* theory of truth (beloved by Hegel among others) argues that the truth of a proposition should be judged by its coherence with other propositions in a broader picture or system. This coherence theory is rated most highly by system builders.

In its simplest form the *pragmatic* theory of truth states simply that what is true is what works in practice. End of story. Perhaps the deepest understanding equates truth with integrity. I have argued elsewhere and above that it was the *integrity* of the early practitioners of 'natural philosophy' (science) that gave them the high ground as against the astrologers, the alchemists, the transmuters etc.

Now within the orbit of the correspondence theory of truth – encompassing the objectivity model of enlightenment science – the question raised is whether a proposition is true or false; whether it correctly describes 'the facts out there'. The unspoken, unrecognised assumption being made is that a 'true' statement is more helpful than a 'false' one.

Putting to one side the question of coherence with a bigger picture and recognising *helpful* (or not) as the important issue for the explorer, the correspondence theory of truth can be viewed as a sub-set of the pragmatic theory of truth: that which advances understanding, wisdom even – what works. In many instances correspondence with the assumed facts will indeed also be helpful to understanding the issues under consideration.

THE BIGGEST PICTURE

Talking of coherence with a bigger picture leads ultimately to asking very wide questions like "What's it all about?"

Later on my own attempted answer to this. In the meantime a big question that has troubled very many people from (i suspect) our remote ancestors to theologians, philosophers, scientists and those people able to take the time to wonder ... where did the Universe come from?

The now generally accepted big bang theory doesn't answer the question but it has focused the debate. The two leading contenders briefly described.

The view endorsed by most, but not all, religions is that an external being or creator, usually called God, created the Universe for His (sic) purposes. After that there are different and vigorously debated views over the extent to which the creator was concerned with, and involved with, His creation; whether He planned to offer prospects of eternity for its (human) inhabitants. Albert Einstein provides an interesting example, endorsing a creator God who "does not play dice"[23] yet rejecting as hubris any notion that the individual human ego should survive death[24].

In contrast to this some scientists taking an atheist position such as Stephen Hawking[25] picture a mechanical yet still wondrous Universe that just popped into existence, complete with its 'laws' (read: patterns) from a no-space, no-matter situation. One cannot even say 'before that' since on this view there was no time either 'until' the big bang!

The above are the two foremost understandings though others such as continuous ongoing existence since forever (no creation) and a world only six thousand years old remain as realities for some.

Now following through on the insight of Arthur Schopenhauer that the Universe has as dynamic, willing inside, complementing its material, observable outside, it is possible to argue that the Universe in which we find ourselves (and possibly other Universes?) willed itself into existence in pursuit of *fulfilment* in and through self-experiencing complexity.

No absolute claim for this view of reality of course. Later, when considering the issue of tolerance and intolerance in the light of co-existing yet incommensurate objective realities (brought forth worlds) it can take its place amongst them.

RECIPROCITY

In the Natural World Story of *Values for Our Time* it was argued that the sixth pattern of our Universe – its dual aspects, its 'inside' and 'outside' – cannot be exempt from the fourth pattern: that all interactions are reciprocal.

Thus, just as matter affects mind in various ways (chemical substances for example) so mind must affect matter, even if the effects can be ignored in many 'normal' circumstances. This is one reason why the model of enlightenment science has experienced such difficulty with paranormal phenomena. Some of the issues were examined by Lawrence Le Shan in *The Medium, The Mystic and The Physicist*[26].

One way of stating this effect is that both belief and scepticism (anti-belief) are capable of shaping the phenomena that they are attempting to observe/measure.

If two investigators, or teams of investigators, are obtaining conflicting results from their research into a particular field of enquiry the presumption within the model is that at least one of them has failed to observe good practice or has incorporated methodological flaws. This need not be the case.

The attitudes with which the project has been approached may have shaped the assumed reality under investigation. It is doubtful, for instance, if a highly sceptical investigation into (say) levitation could ever produce confirming results.

Now this possibility is anathema to enlightenment science with its conceptual model of a single reality that can, in principle, be rationally determined. This philosophy and this science hates uncertainty, ambiguity or other agonistic* situations and will always attempt to close them down or circumvent them.

THE INTERFACE

It has been argued previously[28] that humans – especially modern ego-conscious humans – exist on the interface between individuality and collectivity and that this tension runs through all social and political life.

On the one hand the emphasis is on the human individual, their freedoms, needs and rights – ironically only capable of partial satisfaction due to the collective infrastructure of the society that they may experience as their yoke. On the other hand the collective vision, founded on an idealised notion of community, attempts to mimic the instinctive bonds of 'primitive' social groups, with expected allegiance to the group, the party, the state. In practice 'the collective' ('the general will'[29]) is often expressed through the will and ego of the leader or the leadership group – a selective individualism trumping the collective.

In principle there is a third road which honours the greater whole of the group yet passes back to each member the judgement, the stewardship of the project.

---

* Relevant here are observations by John Gray[27] on the inability of the enlightenment, both politically and economically, to accept challenge to its orthodox assumptions of rationally determined universal values.

V. *Woman Levitating*

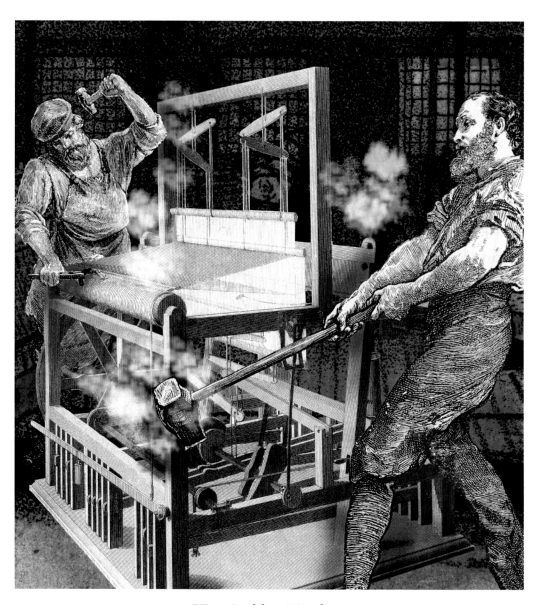

VI. *Luddite Wreckers*

Representative democracy was and is an attempt to follow this road. I argue now that for interlocked mass societies in the present era of modernity representative democracy must fail its intention. Yet hasn't such democracy enjoyed at least partial success, compared to other forms of mass social organisation? That depends on how one defines success: the imperial projects of the Western European democracies; the carnage of the First World War; the Great Depression? Not to mention the impact of powerful lobbies and an ideological media.

Overlooking these little matters and taking the case of England as closest to home, the political system could call on the social capital of English civil society with fair play[30] as the dominant mode most of the time. In regard to class tensions a combination of deference and sullen resentment predominated, with only rare examples of militant action. For its part the establishment, though capable of brutality at times (e.g. Peterloo, Orgreave), was just agile enough to respond to social pressures most of the time. Meanwhile the benefits of a growing and changing economy were gradually trickling down, with the most exploited underclass now out of sight elsewhere in the world. In 1957 Harold Macmillan felt able to claim: "You never had it so good"[31].

That was before modernity really took hold. Before considering the whole project of Neoliberal modernity and the role of enlightenment science within that project, a further look at the issue of social organisation and the tensions around collectivity and autonomy, the group and the individual. [N.B. Plate VII]

SOCIAL TYPES AND MODES

In *The Social Contract*[32] the paleo anthropologist and acute observer of animals Robert Ardrey sheds light on the interactions between groups and their members, between power and responsibility, especially among our nearest cousins the great apes. Ardrey's key concepts of order and disorder correspond roughly to the notions of collectivity and autonomy discussed here. Further, he emphasises the importance of the leaderful Alpha in the group structure of social animals. Here there is a close correspondence with the Divergent – Convergent interaction in *Devolve!* social theory[33]

Rather than viewing these contrasting types negatively as power hierarchies it is necessary to emphasise their complementary functions in all social structures. This is explained more fully in the source just given.

Now for the greater part of human pre-history social groups were small and all members would have known each other, as is still the case among some peoples in our own times. Functional and appropriate social structures, supported by foundational myths, would be, were and are essential for ongoing stability over many generations – perhaps 40,000 years in the case of Australian native peoples.

Jean-Jacques Rousseau[34] is claimed to have pictured 'primitive' man (projecting the autonomous individual back into a social past) as 'the noble savage' – as yet undamaged

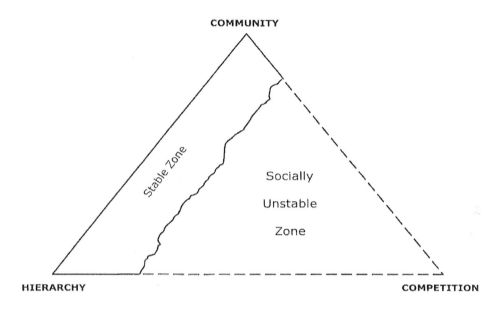

SOCIAL MAPPING: THE TSA TRIANGLE
Insect, Animal and Traditional Human Social Groups

COMMUNITY

Stable Zone

Socially Unstable Zone

HIERARCHY

COMPETITION

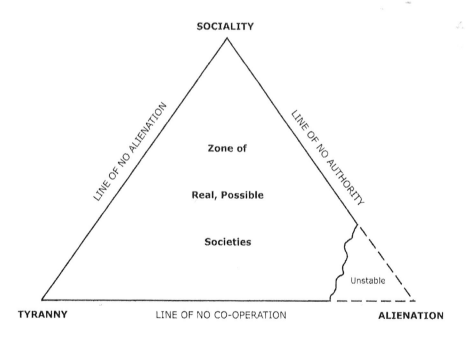

SOCIAL MAPPING: THE TSA TRIANGLE
Modern Large Scale Human Societies

SOCIALITY

LINE OF NO ALIENATION

LINE OF NO AUTHORITY

Zone of

Real, Possible

Societies

Unstable

TYRANNY

LINE OF NO CO-OPERATION

ALIENATION

VII.

and unconstrained by the chains of civilisation. (Compare Sigmund Freud: "civilisation is based on repression of the instincts".) [Rousseau's actual position was more complex.]

In contrast, Thomas Hobbes[35] pictured a past (again of individuals) which was a war of all against all, in which life was "solitary, poor, nasty, brutish and short". He argued that the strong central state, with authority invested in its ruler, was essential to curb our behaviours.

Leaving aside the common lack of understanding of the complexity and structure of social groups, which of these visions is a better approximation to the lived situations? The surprising answer is both of them. In The Social Story of *Values for Our Time*[36] It was argued that both individuals and groups, upon certain triggers, can flip from one mode of behaviour to another. Some examples were given of the various modes. Field studies of actual tribes and native peoples have indicated a wide range of social practices and social norms, ranging from near idyllic to horrific (as judged by external observers).

THE SIZE QUESTION

So far there has only been indirect reference to the *size* of social groups as a factor in their stability and viability. It was however noted earlier that the development of agriculture enabled the formation of mass societies – with some significant consequences.

In *The Breakdown of Nations* Leopold Kohr[37] (who influenced Schumacher) argued that authentic human social organisation is not possible in nation states with mass populations. Today, in this age of modernity, human 'civilisation' is moving beyond the era of quasi-autonomous nation states to the 'global village': an interlocked Neoliberal society and economy with its own internal logic and momentum beyond the control of human actors, possessing an inherent instability. As philosopher John Gray has observed[38]: "A more fragmented, less integrated world is actually more stable: nobody wants to hear that."

Add to this the equally serious implications of technologies gone beyond social control, for which enlightenment science must bear a heavy responsibility through its secondary myth of being values-free.

A deeper critique of human mass society is put forward in the works of John M. Gowdy and Lisi Krall[39] In a recent article in *The Ecological Citizen*[40] under the title *The Economic Legacy of The Holocene* Lizi Krall brings an economic perspective to the ecological impact of the establishment of agriculture (including animal husbandry) that takes the critique to an entirely new level – or maybe depth.

In this project she acknowledges the influence of her (by then dying) step-father Paul Shepard.

Professor Paul Shepard was one of the pioneers of deep ecology and a champion of Pleistocene, modest scaled, pre-agriculture human societies[41].

Professor Krall's central thesis is that it was the division of labour (a key concept in economics) that transformed these agricultural societies into 'superorganisms' with a dynamic of their own beyond the control of individual human actors. In this radical approach purely cultural assumptions are challenged by highlighting the evidence that some species of insects such as leaf cutter ants had long before adopted division of labour to become expansive and formidable superorganisms. Three implications are drawn out in the article (and in related publications)[42]: -

➢ First, that within social superorganisms essentially human aims and intentions are no longer in control of human destiny.

➢ Second, that the de-sacralisation of the world within certain belief systems (e.g. gods beyond nature) could have been re-enforced by the economic dimension. 'Uncontrolled' nature (e.g. weeds and predators) was now understood as a threat to social order, while other flora and fauna could become 'resources'.

➢ Third, Lisi Krall argues that the root of modernity should not only be sought in early capitalism, the nation state or enlightenment science: it should also be viewed as a consequence of the agricultural catastrophe.

Taken as a whole this perspective is quite revolutionary. If valid it sounds the death knell of the Socratic optimism regarding reason and progress that ultimately underpins the enlightenment. It also has implications when considering the scale and structure of social organisation in future situations.

[As an aside, the phenomenon of social outcomes differing from individual intentions may be observed well below the level of the superorganism ascribed to post-agriculture human societies. The famous 'invisible hand' of Adam Smith[43] put a positive spin on the effect. It could equally be applied to a fire in a night club (say) where desperate individual efforts to get out fast contribute to a collective disaster.]

THE SCIENCE DEBATES

Focussing again now on enlightenment science, one of the three pillars upon which global modernity stands.

The narrative so far has traced the historical roots of its commitment to an objective, determined, rule bound and (in principal) discoverable reality 'out there', independent of any observers, of supposed subjective bias; rejecting any 'internal' creative forces. It has already been argued that the orthodox consensus which defends this body of assumptions has the characteristics of a priesthood and is fairly described as such.

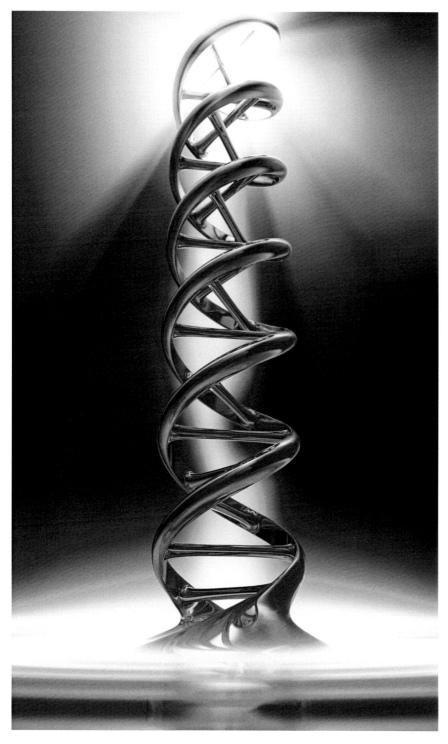

VIII.   *Double Helix Model*

The model of enlightenment science is now under challenge: not just from inconvenient 'facts' (which should lead to reworking of the scientific model in the manner indicated by Thomas Kuhn[44]) but from questioning of its fundamental assumptions. For narrative purposes the challenges may be divided into various approaches.

First, maverick (i.e. well outside the consensus) viewpoints, arguments and models which often fail to stand up to investigations carried out with integrity but which should none the less be considered for any kernels of wisdom.

Second, challenges thrown up by practitioners initially committed to the assumptions of the model but with too much integrity to 'fudge' conformity until and unless a credible resolution of their apparent model-breaking interpretations can be advanced.

Third, some lines of enquiry have reached a situation where there are various disputed interpretations of observed data or mathematical models such that there is no current consensus as to what they actually mean. Quantum mechanics is a prime example.

Fourth, those cases where propositions put forward in the spirit of scientific enquiry are in breach of one or more of the axioms of the orthodox model from the start.

Starting at the maverick end of the spectrum the (now defunct) Natural Philosophy Alliance embraced a wide diversity of bodies including The Flat Earth Society, The Magi Society and The Institute for Creation Research...

Following its collapse in 2014, its partial successor the John Chappell Natural Philosophy Society or CNPS[45] appears to be more science focussed. One of its critiques of the orthodox model revolves around (flaws in) Albert Einstein's relativity theories and the Michelson-Morley experiment (challenging speed of light conclusions). Another one concerns the prospects for a unified field theory. The contributions/calculations of Roger J Anderton and David Tombe[46] are worthy of examination even if they eventually fail (your) credibility/integrity test. The same can be said of challenges to climate change and to human impact predictions. (The irony in this last case is that the mainstream orthodoxy has also been in denial.)

One of the revelations that emerge from this interaction of maverick and orthodox science is that the priesthood appears to have downplayed or even airbrushed out of the narrative some significant contributors to the development of ideas. An example of this was Roger Joseph Boscovitch (1711 – 1787)[47] who some claim to be the father of modern atomic physics. According to Roger Anderton such giants as Faraday, Maxwell and Kelvin were influenced by his ideas. It was only post Einstein that Boscovitch became obscure.

Among many achievements (he was a real polymath) Boscovitch was proposing a unified field theory around 150 years before Einstein.

CHALLENGES FROM WITHIN

Within the various branches of mainstream science the perspective of Systems Theory was one of the most significant developments of the twentieth century. Its development and eventual acceptance owed much to the efforts of Gregory Bateson (1904 – 1980)[48]. Fritjof Capra[49], in an introduction to Florence Bateson's film *An Ecology of Mind,* pointed out Bateson's contributions to a range of sciences and his pioneering of inter-disciplinary cognitive science. Capra emphasised that Bateson's approach "replaced the Newtonian metaphor of the world as a machine with the metaphor of the network" – best thought of in terms of relationships, connections, patterns and context rather than in terms of objects obeying laws. Gregory Bateson was to influence a range of critical thinkers, some of them referred to below, who in turn came to challenge the core assumptions of orthodox science.

The Santa Fe Institute[50] has provided a 'nursery' for contributions to radical scientific theories and ideas. These include Complexity Theory, Chaos Theory and Information Theory which between them have challenged orthodox ideas across several disciplines. One of these areas has been evolutionary biology.

Stuart Kauffman[51] has made a case for the emergence of autocatalytic (self-reproducing) proteins once there is a critical level of complexity among organic networks – even when no RNA replicators are present. The implication is that Darwinian 'blind' natural selection must be supplemented by, and preceded by, spontaneous self-creation of organic life from complexity – the norm under favourable conditions rather than an exceptional accident. Needless to say, this line of argument is heretical from the standpoint of evolutionary biology rooted in Neo-Darwinian determinism and adaptionism. For an example of criticism of Kauffman's conclusions on complexity see Roger Sampson[52].

In further work Stuart Kauffman presents a hypothesis for the emergence of mind and consciousness based on partially quantum conditions. The mathematical physicist and philosopher of science Roger Penrose has also argued for quantum wave function collapse being implicated in the phenomenon of consciousness[53].

AUTOPOIESIS

The Chilean biologists Humberto Maturana (b1928) and Francisco Varela (1946-2001) went further with their research based theory of Autopoiesis (self-making)[54] in asserting that biological entities are capable of self-producing the organisational structures that validate them as living beings.

The most radical implication of Autopoiesis is not just that the organism self-creates itself into living existence but that it creates (constructs), through its relationship with its environment, the nature of what is 'out there'. In the philosophy of science this means that the notion of an objective reality, independent of the actor or observer, cannot be supported by empirical observation. This accords with some of the interpretations of quantum mechanics such as Heisenberg's uncertainty principle[55] (See further discussion later). To quote Karl Marx out of context "all that is solid melts into air".

The conclusion of Maturana and Varela is that we actually create our realities; we "bring forth worlds with each other". (As noted earlier none of this denies the usefulness of pragmatic objectivity – say making allowance for the distance from us of a person or thing in judging their size – in our daily lives.)

Now this challenge to the foundational assumption of an objective reality beyond our lived in 'world of appearances' – with its roots going back to Newton, Descartes, Plato and Hebrew theology – was bound to provoke a hostile reaction from orthodox (model defending) practitioners of science. Autopoiesis is considered heretical by the mainstream with allegations of solipsism and flawed interpretation.

None-the-less their radical theory was based in really solid research conducted with integrity. Their conclusions have also chimed with other significant investigators and thinkers. These have included Lynn Margulis (1938-2011)[56]. Her research based work on symbiosis between microbial elements in the formation of cells is now generally accepted. However her further claim that symbiogenesis is a more general evolutionary force and may be a more significant factor in the evolution of life forms than Darwinian selection of random gene mutations … remains heretical from the viewpoint of 'orthodox' evolutionary biologists. It enjoys more support from ecologists working in the field – that is in nature rather than in the laboratory.

Richard Lewontin (b1929)[57], an evolutionary biologist and geneticist, is also critical of genetic determinism. He has challenged the Neo-Darwinist view of the one directional effect of environments on the survival of organisms. Lewontin argues instead that there is a two way relation in which the organism actively constructs its environment. (Certainly true of Homo sapiens today!)

THE SYMBOLIC MIND

Terrence Deacon (b1950)[58] is a neuro-anthropologist who has made significant contributions to the evolution debate at several levels. Influenced by the Pragmatic school of philosophy, especially C.S. Pierce[59] and by Quantum Mechanics, Deacon identifies the basis of self-organisation that can, under suitable conditions, enable the emergence of protolife.

Also of relevance for our wider discussion is his thesis on how the human mind represents its environment. His book *The symbolic Species: The Co-evolution of Language and The Brain*[60] argues that for humans the world is represented and mediated though symbols.

Terrence Deacon notes that, as a symbolic species "we seem to be preoccupied with ends": both in a search for ultimate meaning, for purpose, in the Universe and in responding to our own eventual deaths. He argues that our animal evolution did not include selection for these traits.

Symbolic representation 'allows' a new self-determination. Created models of possible futures based on fragments of real experiences generate in response "independent adaptive behaviours". These actions, answering to symbolically predicted events can override biologically based responses to situations.

Terrence Deacon argues that contrasting 'reason' – inference and model building towards a symbolised goal – with our instinctive desires and compulsions does not demonstrate a free will able to triumph over blind passions. Rather, there is a tension between contrasting compulsions. Further, the drive towards symbolic goals can arise from a "vast variety" of initial triggers.

Symbolic thinking, according to Deacon, goes much further than modelling and predicting events in the world. It "projects itself into what it models". It adds a teleological dimension, interpreting events as "the working out of a divine plan". Nothing is neutral, valid on its own terms. This goes way beyond symbolic interpretations of human situations: "all the Universe has become a symbol".

Terrence Deacon presses the point. We are not just a species that uses symbols: this symbolic adaptation has infected us "like a mind virus". All things are now understood as symbols. We are become the carriers through which this virus "propagates itself throughout the world".

FEAR OF DEATH, FEAR OF FALLING

Symbolic models are not simply random. The human inability to handle death has already been suggested as a factor in the emergence of belief in that other world.

With this further understanding of the symbolic mind we can now make a distinction between the biological fear of death when it is seconds or minutes away and the fear of death as an *idea*.

Perhaps equally vital for the self-aware mind is the need for bearings, for an anchor point. At a physical level the phenomenon of sea sickness and the experience of giddiness on fairground roundabouts are caused by the loss of a fixed horizon and/or a stable reference point in our sense of balance. [N.B. Plate IX]

IX.   *An effect of loss of bearings!*

At the symbolic level the desire for an anchor point is very powerful and it requires an act of courage to overcome this 'fear of falling'. One aspect of this is widespread hostility to the notion of a relative Universe: the understanding that there are no absolutes. (The notion, discussed later, of incommensurate objective realities can generate the same reaction.)

Our need for meaning, for bearings, extends across both our social realities and our moralities. If there are no absolutes how can i prove that i am right and you are wrong? Or that some behaviours are beyond the pale?

Terrence Deacon points out that a consequence of absolutes in our symbolic realities is that clashes of these absolutes has caused, does cause, the most appalling blood baths and oppressions.

THE QUANTUM ENIGMA

A challenge to the orthodox model of enlightenment science from the start of the twentieth century has been quantum theory – or perhaps we should say theories. The parallels with the early Christian Church – as it was increasingly looked to as the new power in the land, the measure of all things – are quite striking. The attempts to define and defend orthodoxy, to condemn heresy, run through both narratives.

Some of the emerging tensions were in the area of classical physics but they spilled over into the realm of metaphysics ('beyond physics'). The attempt to defend a rational (logic following) mechanical Universe became entangled with Darwinian evolution and the emergence of life; with broad ecological perspectives; with the cognitive and social sciences; with the nature of the mind and consciousness. Several philosophers have pointed out that the waters have been muddied by unfortunate terminology. For example, Newton did not discover any laws: he observed some apparently consistent patterns which might, or might not, be ordained by some great Law Giver. Likewise Roger Anderton quotes Eddington[61] as remarking that the second 'law' of thermodynamics (the entropy principle) should be regarded as a working hypothesis rather than an article of faith.

The quantum story began with attempts to account for discrepancies between certain observed phenomena and the 'laws' of classical science. The details of the subsequent discoveries and explanations are not the main focus of this essay. Their impacts on the core model of enlightenment science, its defenders and its challengers, certainly are.

The first quantum explanations by Max Planck, Albert Einstein and others (now referred to as old quantum theory) were revolutionary at the time but with hindsight seemed to confirm that the Universe (at the microscopic level) was 'lumpy' rather than a continuous plasma in which everything was possible.

X.   *Isaac Newton by William Blake*

However, attempts to 'fine tune' the model and account for a widening range of problematical findings led to new quantum theory and quantum mechanics. These problems have included Heisenberg's uncertainty principle, wave-particle duality, entanglement and non-locality. The situation in the twenty first century is that the quantum Universe can be described by mathematical equations but there is no agreement on what these equations actually mean. According to a quote attributed to David Mermin[62] the advice to young researchers attempting to grapple with the meaning of it all is "shut up and do the maths".

A current (2018) Wikipedia article on quantum mechanics lists no less than fourteen different explanations of what the equations mean in 'reality'.

An important (metaphysical!) interpretation of this situation is that the underlying assumption of enlightenment science – that it is (in principle) working towards a complete understanding of the objective reality 'out there' – is not tenable. A Santa Fe Institute paper by Professor David Wolpert[63] establishes that total scientific knowledge of everything is not achievable.

As enlightenment science attempts to probe deeper and deeper into 'objective reality', not just in the area of quantum mechanics, the complexity challenges the model itself. A justifiable metaphor is the apocryphal story of the Tower of Babel, where the peoples of the world (read: scientists of the world) resolved to build a great tower stretching up to heaven (read: to objective truth). Because they all had different languages (read: interpretations) the project ended in chaos and the tower collapsed.

EXTERNAL – INTERNAL

Regarding quantum theory there has been unease for many decades across a wide range of physics theorists and philosophers of science. A widely held view implied that the quantum model as it stood was incomplete: that there were hidden variables waiting to be discovered. Albert Einstein was expressing this view from the 1920's onwards.

However, motivating these concerns were two very different world views and agendas. For some the objective was to 'reduce' probabilistic and indeterminate descriptions to a determinist model consistent with the core assumptions of classical science. For others the model was pointing beyond the externalities of a mechanical Universe towards the possibilities of internal wisdoms.

The physicist and (ultimately) metaphysician David Bohm[64] was distinctive in spanning both of these aspirations. Bohm's early collaboration with Einstein, his notable scientific discoveries, his revival of De Broglie's notion of pilot waves as a quantum possibility established his reputation (albeit a controversial one) as a significant scientist.

Alongside this conventional path, Bohm was increasingly dis-satisfied with the generally accepted models of quantum mechanics and was searching for deeper explanations. This eventually gave rise to his notion of an implicate order[65] in the Universe, underlying and complementing the explicate order amenable to scientific measurement.

As his life course progressed, Bohm moved beyond enlightenment science to wisdom, as indicated by his long relationship with Jiddu Krishnamurti[66] and some of his later publications.

Needless to say, this stepping beyond the model led to Bohm being shunned by the establishment for considerable periods, although his scientific pedigree meant that he could not be totally excommunicated.

In terms of the central thread of this essay the notion of an implicate order touches on Schopenhauer's critical insight that our Universe (like us) has a passionate inside as the complement of its/our observable outside.

David Bohm arguably didn't quite go all the way: it seems he still wanted to see the implicate order in terms of deep physical reality. This might be unfair: Bohm did argue for the interconnectedness of mind and matter. In a critical review Martin Gardner[67] picked up on Bohm's apparent remark that "even the electron is informed with a certain level of mind". For Gardner this was evidence that Bohm "flirted with panpsychism".

SHELDRAKE

Moving from physics to biology, another thinker excommunicated by the priesthood for heresy, mentioned in passing earlier in the story, is Rupert Sheldrake.

The concept of morphogenic fields – their ability to guide the development of embryos, correct for damage events and support evolutionary change – was advancing during the early decades of the last century. It came to be eclipsed by the alternative model of gene expression and translation being argued for as Neo-Darwinism became predominant in biology.

More recently, with advances in the theory and methodology of molecular biology, fresh evidence for the reality and role of morphogenic fields has brought this approach to our understanding of both embryonic development and evolution back into favour[68].

Sheldrake's more radical and challenging hypothesis of morphic fields – that developing organisms or crystals or problem solvers can draw on memories of how it was done before in another time or place – was the basis of his controversial book *A New Science of Life*, first published in 1981[69].

Rupert Sheldrake, originally a research botanist 'by trade', made significant contributions to the chemistry of plant biology in his early career. His growing understanding that Darwinian biology could not answer the broader questions of plant development set him on a path that would eventually challenge many of the core assumptions of classical science. This alone would have led to his being side-lined by the orthodox establishment, as others have been over the generations. His greater crime was to go over the heads of that establishment and communicate directly to a wider public.

The New Science of Life contains as an appendix a dialogue between Sheldrake and David Bohm[70]. This is highly recommended reading. It reveals that their understandings were closely aligned in many respects.

Further, Bohm's implicate order is actually more radical since it implies irrevocably the inside of the Universe whereas Rupert Sheldrake at that stage was 'only' putting forward a disprovable[71] hypothesis about a particular phenomenon, certainly no stranger than entanglement (say) in quantum mechanics. It can be noted that the physicist Lee Smolin[72] has advanced the notion of precedence in quantum theory, which implies the influence of past events on the present, as does the concept of morphic fields.

So why the extreme hostility to Rupert Sheldrake? One reason has already been given above. Another is that David Bohm (in particular) had such a powerful reputation as a ground breaking scientist that the response of ignoring his later 'folly' was preferred by most defenders of orthodoxy. I suggest that there is a third reason.

The quantum debates are in a sense open and highly contested. In biology by contrast the mechanistic and determinist model of the Neo-Darwinists still predominates despite evidence for active and creative self-development of living forms referred to in the life work of notable researchers and theorisers.

Rupert Sheldrake has since committed other blasphemies. Perhaps more fundamental than his investigations of events that are generally classified as paranormal[73] has been his questioning of some of the fundamentals of enlightenment science including the assumed universal constants[74]

LANCELOT WHYTE

So far this challenging of enlightenment science, naming its orthodoxy as a priesthood, has not made clear enough its role as one of the three pillars of modernity. Hence the diagram at Plate 12 of *Values for Our Time* must be seen as incomplete: it recognised the roles of the market and the state yet not that of enlightenment science.

Modernity, so defined[75], is arguably leading Homo sapiens to the abyss: due to take a large part of the biosphere (many species and ecosystems) down with it. There is today a widening awareness of the predicament – yet only in terms of the evident symptoms, not the fundamentals.

Lancelot Law Whyte was a polymath who stood just outside the orthodox mainstream of science. As well as being a theoretical physicist he was also a historian of science and a philosopher.

Whyte was one of the few thinkers of his generation to draw attention to the significance of Roger Joseph Boscovitch. Like Boscovitch he sought to explore a unified field theory.

According to Roger Anderton[76] there was a connection between the downplaying of Boscovitch and Whyte himself (plus even the later Einstein) and the 'fade out' of the exploration of unified field theory.

Whyte's argument for *Internal Factors in Evolution*[77] both challenges Neo-Darwinian determinism in biology and chimes with the conclusions of a wide range of researchers, some of them reported on above. Further, it represents a step in acknowledging the internal aspect of our Universe, as does Bohm's implicate order and Sheldrake's morphogenic fields – and your own experience of yourself.

Lancelot Whyte is recognised as a philosopher as well as a scientist. In *The Next Development in Man*[78] he argued for a new science. As noted in *Values for Our Time*[79] this should be *integrative* across all wisdom; about *process* rather than 'facts'; socially and *morally embedded* rather than values neutral.

How far have we come? To some extent a more inter-disciplinary approach has forced itself upon researchers and theorisers in the wake of complexity theory and other challenges. Some branches of science have been resistant, economics being an extreme example. (With honourable exceptions such as Nicholas Georgescu-Roegan[80].)

Regarding the call for a science of process there have been some acknowledgements yet the mantra of 'an objective reality of hard facts' continues to retain sacred status among defenders of the orthodoxy.

Values embedded science? See below.

QUANTUM OBJECTIVITY

The notion of pragmatic objectivity has previously been offered in contrast to the absolute existence of an objective world 'out there' as claimed by enlightenment science. The following elaboration may be helpful for some.

The patterns described by Isaac Newton and others in the model of classical science remain *approximately* true in the wake of the hypotheses of relativity and quantum mechanics. Apples still do (usually) fall to earth. It is only at the limits of scale, so to speak, that the classical model breaks down.

The classical notion of objectivity would remain useful for many everyday purposes. Although not an exact parallel it could be argued that at the limits of sensitivity the 'quantum interaction' of object and observer takes place.

Now very few scientists operating within the orthodox model would be satisfied with the above explanation – and they might be justified. Meanwhile the notion of a single, universal objective reality portraying a determined Universe has been questioned by too many investigators of high integrity. So there is a need to explore a broader understanding.

BROUGHT FORTH OBJECTIVITY

One starting point is the insight of Terrence Deacon, referred to previously[81], that we have become the symbolic animal, our minds comprehending all things through symbols. The orthodox model would, of course, wish to deny this challenge to their 'facts'. Compare this to the argument of Patrick Curry that "metaphor is both relational and dialogical ... the agency of the other party is obvious"[82] and the refusal of orthodox science to accept that its 'facts' are metaphorical.

This leads on to the insight developed from the work of Maturana and Varela already noted earlier[83] – that we create our realities; "bring forth worlds with each other".

It follows that *within* each community of thought there will be an understood reality that can be considered objective. It would be arrogant and meaningless to say to a devout Christian (say) "your god does not exist" (as i once used to do!).

Thus we can now recognise that the orthodoxy of enlightenment science is another such community of thought which has "brought forth" its objective world. There is an irony in its sceptical method since a shorthand notation is that belief creates (brings forth) worlds and scepticism destroys them. The scepticism is *not* applied to its core model.

Does that mean that challenging or denigrating enlightenment science (as distinct from partial criticisms) is insolent? The defence that i would offer is that *if* enlightenment science is one of the three pillars of modernity; today of Neoliberal modernity (you might not agree), then the consequences for all life on this planet justify any of us who have come to understand the situation acting to make clear its historical and philosophical foundations.

TOLERANCE AND INTOLERANCE

The other aspect of enlightenment science is the absoluteness of its claim: "This is how it really is – all other views are at best mistaken; at worst heresy."

This stance finds a close parallel in the age of scholasticism. The bones of John Wycliffe were dug up and burnt. In Bohemia one of his followers, Huss, was burnt alive. (In this context Rupert Sheldrake has got off quite lightly!)

Now in many parts of the world today there is tolerance between different communities of thought and the worlds that they have brought forth – both religious and secular. Does this imply acceptance of a relative Universe? Another reading would be of parallel worlds, each objective and absolute in their own terms, with no rational basis for judging between them. This plurality of values combined with mutual tolerance defines the agonistic liberalism argued for by John Gray[84].

This mutual tolerance is anathema to all fundamentalists who know that theirs is the true understanding: whether the orthodoxy of endless growth (hence the vitriolic hostility to Malthus) or the adherents of (say) Islamic State.

So – even as the ecosphere slides towards transition (a deliberate euphemism) – the ideological front line among humans today is not between this or that brought forth world, this or that understanding, but between the relative and the absolute; between tolerance and unforgiving conviction.

It behoves us to watch our language.

THE VALUES QUESTION

Now for many people going about their everyday lives (that's most of us) some of the above issues might be dismissed as arguments within science. Not so with Whyte's third challenge.

The pretence of science – as the midwife of technology and thus the servant of modernity – to be values free is both dishonest and terrifying. In an earlier essay it was noted that Albert Einstein's alleged response to the detonation of the first atomic bomb was: "I wish I had been a locksmith"[85]. Only recently have some scientists taken a principled stand against certain developments having serious ecological consequences. Even here their own roles in the technologies (terminator genes for example) may be opaque.

The detonations at Hiroshima and Nagasaki 'only' destroyed two cities (with their civilian populations supposedly protected under the Geneva Convention). Today the headlong rush of science-led technologies into so many uncharted waters without any social accountability or broader overview is helping to ensure that the dynamic of modernity has become unstoppable – until it hits the buffers of the natural world. A wide range of critical wisdoms have argued along these lines[86]. As explored below, the final stages of our human collapse may well have terrifying manifestations.

THE ROMANTIC REACTION

One of the tragedies of the last few centuries has been the cleavage between enlightenment science and the humanities. Within this latter tradition the alarm bells were ringing at an early stage of the rise of the new scientific, rationalistic, instrumentalist ethos.

The romantic reaction sought to respond to these dominant attitudes as science and technology seemed to sweep all before them.

The challenge inspired creativity from a wide range of contributors, including as examples William Blake and Johann Wolfgang von Goethe. The romantics were ahead of most of us in seeing that modernity was indeed striking a Faustian bargain. The summary in a philosophy handbook[87] notes that "Faust sells his soul to the devil, not for money, sex or fame but for the right to control nature..."

Another aspect of romanticism was noted earlier: a deep pessimism, with art as the redeeming feature of a hopeless world.

In education today the humanities are increasingly marginalised and in some schools barely taught: after all, what can they do for the bottom line? This is the dire context for the challenge of L.L. Whyte: for us to shape an integrated science.

From the standpoint of those outside the orbit of 'Western' civilisation, of modernity – including traditional peoples – our trajectory was clear from the start. The Cree prophesy[88] puts it thus: "When all the trees have been cut down, when all the animals have been hunted, when all the waters are polluted, when all the air is unsafe to breathe ... only then will you discover you cannot eat money."

There is perhaps a ray of hope from within science itself. This essay has drawn attention to a number of researchers and thinkers who have sought to place their discoveries and theories in a broader context.

From the point of view of the defenders of orthodoxy, the priesthood, they have "strayed from the path" or "gone on to do something else". I would see them as maybe the seedlings of the human-embedded science that Lancelot Whyte was calling for.

SOME KEY POINTS REVIEWED

Before moving forward, a brief reprise of key propositions so far: -

➢ Reluctance among some of our early ancestors to face up to the 'slings and arrows' of life in general and to the miracle of death in particular led to the notion of a 'real world' beyond our actual transient lived experience.

➤ This comforting myth was carried forward through early religions, Platonic rational optimism, Christianity and Scholasticism into enlightenment science as the notion of an objective world.

➤ At almost every stage priesthoods adopted and supported this myth as a tool for intimidation, coercion, exploitation and dominance.

➤ A further development was the denial of social community and social structure in favour of the pre-eminence of the human individual ... who could be guilt tripped, exploited and enticed. (Everlasting life was arguably the first marketed commodity.)

➤ Social structure is complex and organic, evolved for small groups. Our majority/minority responses to the dilemmas of responsibility (potential pain) and power (potential joy) create natural complementary types which transform into hierarchies of dominance and obedience in mass societies.

➤ There is no fixed human nature. Both individuals and groups can 'flip' into different attitude and behaviour modes upon appropriate triggers.

➤ The model of enlightenment science, one of the props of modernity, is now under challenge from without and within.

MORALITY?

Now to approach the is/ought question – comparing descriptions of what exists, how things are, with so called normative issues: how they 'ought' to be.

The assumption of an absolute moral dimension to life has been criticised above and in earlier work. In The Natural World Story of *Values for Our Time*[89] morality was named as the ninth feature of the content of the Universe and identified as arising out of conflicts of purposes. Morality is relative to purpose. The cry "That is morally wrong!" means "It challenges or threatens my/our/His purpose."

Now this essay is a 'moral' criticism of modernity and so of enlightenment science as one of its components. It is not just an argument that science might have its 'facts' wrong or that its descriptions might be flawed in some respects.

This forces me and us (i am hardly alone) to consider our own assumptions about existence and the actions (purposes) that we are moved to pursue. Are we not making moral challenges?

There will be many different starting points for our concerns, sometimes partly unexamined. (Nothing wrong with that: intuition is not infallible but logic is only as good as its starting assumptions. The heart can be wiser than the head.)

What follows is my own present understanding, learnt from so many mentors. I would not wish to lay this on others. Readers will recognise some of the threads from this and earlier essays.

➤ Existence is its own point. It needs no external meaning.

➤ The Universe is no mere object. It experiences itself in its complexity.

➤ From the outside there appears to be a paradox: increasing disorder, declining intropy* yet increasing self-created structural complexity. This raises many as yet unanswered questions.

➤ On the inside of the Universe there is self-experience of growing complexity and fulfilment in the many cycles of activity.

➤ According to some present theories the Universe may run down as its intropy is exhausted; become a 'dead' Universe. But so what? Leaving aside the assumption of linear time, existence is the volume of self-fulfilment 'under the curve', not any goal[90].

➤ Moving to organic life, including ourselves, the internal and external aspects are obvious.

* A positive concept; N.B. Schrodinger's negative entropy.

- All creatures 'do their thing'. *Fulfilment* in doing so is their/our meaning. (Happiness is inevitably transient, often a transcendental aspiration – far removed from world engagement.) [N.B. Plate XI]

- Since there is already fulfilment in the cycles of life, progress is another word for instability.

- Yet change is often forced by organic process (e.g. species competition) into further creative complexity with wider scope for fulfilment.

- Perhaps the best answer to this paradox is the two thresholds concept of Ivan Illich[91]: too little development sets limits to fulfilment; too rapid development can indicate loss of immanence, over-emphasis on transcendence. [N.B. Plate XII] (This can apply in societies as much as in biology.)

- Broadening out the perspective to the entire biosphere, the interacting complexity and the scope for many levels of fulfilment are self-evident.

- The reciprocity of the biosphere demands that no one species becomes super-dominant.

- For any single species the two thresholds principle is again relevant. Inadequate coping with its environment may lead a species to extinction. Over-dominant behaviour can threaten to destabilise that environment.

SPACE GEOGRAPHY: THE ETI TRIANGLE
Existential Attitudes To Life

TRANSCENDENCE

LINE OF EQUANIMITY

LINE OF GOING BEYOND

Range of

Existential Attitudes

within this space

IMMANENCE

LINE OF WORLD ENGAGEMENT

XI.

EXCELLENCE

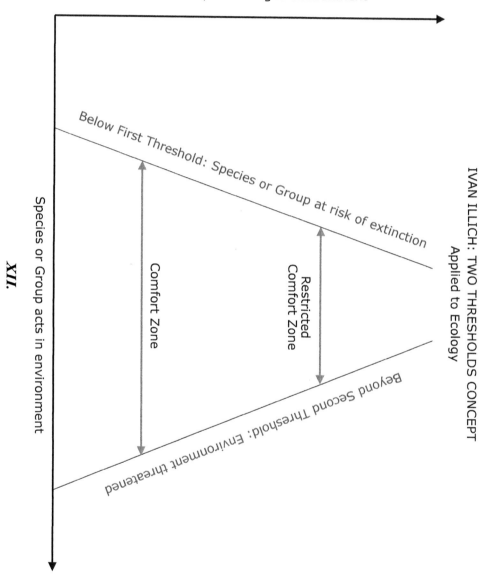

XII.

IVAN ILLICH: TWO THRESHOLDS CONCEPT
Applied to Ecology

Poorer, more fragile environment

Species or Group acts in environment

Below First Threshold: Species or Group at risk of extinction

Beyond Second Threshold: Environment threatened

Comfort Zone

Restricted Comfort Zone

➤ This has been the situation of our species since the birth of agriculture with assured food supplies; population explosions; mass societies; technological dominance; self-justifying values[92]; separation of head from heart, of science from the humanities and our humanity. Finally the mutually re-enforcing triad of mass managerial states beyond peoples; of global economies driven by their internal logic; of enlightenment science claiming to be values free and grasping its funding without question.

Now there is no *absolute* reason why the biosphere on earth should survive with its present level of complexity; why any remaining humans should not yield to non-biological self-perpetuating systems. (Probable/possible future scenarios will be considered later.) Yet conversely there is no good reason why some humans and communities should not adopt the purpose/morality of opposing such scenarios. From their internal perspective the dynamic of modernity can be called immoral and its consequences potentially disastrous.

OUR PREDICAMENT

The motivation for this essay was concern for the biosphere on planet earth and an attempt to understand the factors that threaten it. The runaway 'success' of Homo sapiens and its consequent *impact* on the rest of the biosphere has been revealed as the core issue.

Three questions follow. First, what historical developments have led to our present predicament? Second, what are the drivers of modern trends; what are the mainsprings of modernity? Third, what are the key aspects or dimensions of the resultant impact?

A significant part of the story so far has been attempting to answer the first question. Intertwined with this, giving rise to the title, has been a critique of enlightenment science. Why? Partly because the philosophy of John Gray pointed in that direction. Partly because i have found the arguments of Dr Patrick Curry convincing: that global modernity rests on the three pillars of techno-science, capitalist expropriation and the managerial state. If correct, this answers the second question.

So what about impact? We can perhaps identify three tangible factors and one intangible contributor, each with their advocates. In summary: the greatest human threats to the biosphere, to the network of ecosystems that sustains life, are from dangerous *technology*; from rampant *consumption*; from the level and growth of human *population*; from alienated *values*.

TECHNOLOGY IMPACT

Taking technology first, there is certainly some truth in the arguments. The contribution of fossil fuels to global warming and the ubiquitous plastics finding their way into the oceans are receiving much attention at the time of writing.

Equally serious, although less talked about, are the long term consequences of radioactive nuclear waste. Species loss due to habitat destruction is an issue coming into focus.

However, there is a danger in the conviction that the problem of human impact can be resolved by technical fixes alone without addressing our massive consumption or sheer numbers; of regarding such fixes as a 'get out of jail free' card.

CONSUMPTION IMPACT

Although the roots go much further back in time the growth in human consumption (both in total and per person) over recent centuries has been staggering. This includes both infrastructure consumption and personal consumption.

Infrastructure spans not only 'fixed' structures such as power and communication networks, roads/motorways, rail links, air travel webs but war machines, health machines and much more.

As for personal consumption – that which we apparently control directly by our spending decisions – this once responded to our needs.

In the past century personal consumption has become supply driven rather than demand driven. The logic of 'for profit' production requires that we have to be tempted to buy more and more 'stuff' to keep the wheels from coming off the bus[93]. It does not require much imagination to see that this endless growth mantra is a giant Ponzi scheme. Except that those locked into the system can never admit the obvious. In the words of Kenneth Boulding[94] "anyone who believes exponential growth can go on for ever in a finite world is either a madman or an economist".

POPULATION IMPACT

In 1798 Thomas Robert Malthus first drew attention to the population issue for a successful species[95]. His basic thesis was that population would eventually outstrip food supply unless and until certain checks came into operation to limit population growth. This should have been taken as a reasonable hypothesis even if better information should prove it to be false. Unfortunately (in his first edition) Malthus pointed his finger at the poor (since there were many more of them), making him a hate figure for egalitarians everywhere. I would argue that there was, and is, more to it than that: the enlightenment conviction and ideology of endless progress can brook no bounds. Even today, when the signs seem clear to some of us that humanity as a species and its 'progress' in particular is coming up against so many natural limits ... simply stating the obvious continues to provoke extreme hostility.

When Malthus was writing, worldwide human population was around one billion. By the 1960s world population had risen to three billion and was becoming a subject of open concern and debate. In 1971 Jack Parsons, then deputy director of the Sir David Owen Centre for Population Studies at Cardiff University published *Population versus* Liberty[96]. There were forwards by three prominent politicians: David Renton, Conservative MP and later Peer; Douglas Houghton, Labour MP and later also elevated to the peerage; Lord (Tim) Beaumont, then a Liberal Party supporter. In his forward Lord Beaumont stated: "This ... is a subject which will be moving more and more into the centre of national and international politics."

Then something strange happened. Possibly as a result of an unholy alliance of Left wing 'progressives' and some Christians the population issue was taken out of the arena of public discussion. The topic was suppressed on the BBC for more than three decades. (Jack Parsons' last book, published posthumously, was titled *The Treason of The BBC*[97])

Against this background the Optimum Population Trust (later to become Population Matters[98]) was formed in 1991 by concerned individuals to draw attention to the issues of human population and population growth. OPT/PM has had to endure years of hostility and mis-representation. It has only slowly won a measure of acceptance, aided by high profile patrons such as Sir David Attenborough.

As a consequence, in my view, (i remain a member) there has been a cautious response that has partly failed to respond to the developing situation. Now the work of Population Matters in drawing attention to world human population, advocating and supporting the empowerment of women in overseas countries (notably in Africa), encouraging young first world families to consider 'stopping at two' is beyond reproach.

However the central Population Matters objective is to have less young people born into an overcrowded world. This at a time when many nations and their politicians are grappling with falling birth rates and ageing populations. In addition many of the concerned activists offering 'advice' to others are well past child reproducing age.

OWNING THE PROBLEM

All too often the response to any social problem that demands attention is "someone else should fix it". So daring to say "I own the problem" is both radical and scary. In particular, those of us who have had long and fulfilled lives *and* are very concerned for the world should maybe look ourselves in the mirror: "If you think that there are too many people on the planet – get off it."

[Owning the problem, acting ourselves, rather than looking to 'them' to fix it, is a fundamental challenge to us all that goes way beyond the special case discussed here.

Lobbying governments to reduce carbon emissions when we haven't even draught proofed our houses or cut down on flying (say) can be viewed as hypocrisy.]

Now the above provocative statement is putting it a bit crudely. Individual responsibility means *we* are the stewards with many factors to weigh. Population Matters has always opposed coercive measures and i concur. (There remains an issue with young children being denied birth because high consuming older humans remain greedy for life.)

However, we do need *access* to this choice. Here is where those arguing that we need to face up to both the population and consumption dimensions of human impact have work to do. Plate XIII attempts to illuminate the situation.

In a social world where human rights have become almost synonymous with civilisation it is staggering that the civil right to exit at a time of one's choosing, with social approval and support, does not exist. (This is not a conversation about suicide, which is a rejection of life, but of responsible decisions to make way for all life going forward. Nor is it a medical matter: campaigns to allow those terminally ill or with appalling quality of life to make their exit are now making some progress[99] – often in the face of opposition from medical priesthoods.)

THE RIGHT TO EXIT

Pioneers in any social field can expect to face both widespread hostility and political and legal repression. The women's suffrage movement in England was a classic example. In the case now considered what could be at stake is a more balanced and more modest human population going forward.

If the civil right to exit is the final human rights crusade then its champion is already with us. Exit International[100] now has chapters and supporters in several countries, in large part due to the persistence of its early driving force Dr Philip Nitschke[101].

If Population Matters and similar organisations are to have credible and coherent responses to the human impact of both growing and ageing populations then building bridges with Exit International and other like movements that may emerge will need to form part of their strategies: regarding them as 'doing something else' will in the medium term limit their own effectiveness in the task that they have set themselves.

Both groupings aim for non-coercive strategies with empowerment over personal decisions as routes to fewer humans on this planet in future.

POPULATION, CONSUMPTION and LONGEVITY - Visual Representations (not to scale)

Actual World Population Numbers
(source: World Population Clock)

First World Population: 1 Billion People

Rest of World Population
6.4 Billion People

World Equivalent Population Numbers
Taking account of consumption

Fraction of these beyond Seventy Years
2 Billion People Equivalent

First World Population
12 Billion People Equivalent
(source: Physics fact book/money)

Rest of World Population
6.4 Billion People Equivalent

XIII.

Albert Einstein is reported to have said "It is tasteless to prolong life artificially. [When] it is time to go i will do it elegantly."

XIV. *Albert Einstein*

THE UNDERLYING VALUES

Already this review of total human impact on the planet is moving beyond the tangible factors of technology, consumption and numbers to the intangible: cultures and their values. If the culture of modernity – in which we are all immersed – can be summed up in a couple of words then the best labels are hubris and arrogance. (One dictionary defines hubris as insolent pride.) Before exploring the appropriate values for any human culture in harmony with the biosphere, with the world around it, there is need to consider some future scenarios. Taking a timespan of fifty years as a limit of vision, three possible future roads are here put forward.

First, that the integrated and overlocking worldwide economic and cultural system defined here as modernity continues to hold together, albeit under growing pressure with at the margins increasing tensions, resource conflicts and dissolution into warlord fiefdoms (of which the drugs cartels are a precursor). *Second*, a relatively gradual collapse with regional power centres presiding over zonal networks and attempting to maintain both economic infrastructure and social cohesion even as the human death rate climbs steeply and the biosphere is scavenged and ravaged. *Third*, a more dramatic collapse of 'civilisation' as we know it with an era of panic and chaos, major damage to the biosphere in the short term and a reduction in total human population in the range of 95% to 99%. It is contended that even in this extreme case *some* humans will survive into that very different world.

Against these hypothetical scenarios a caution and a clarification. Modern humans have proved themselves to be resourceful under duress and their institutions resilient in a manner that has confounded many predictions.

Three counterpoints in response to this.

The first is that the scope of the converging threats to the model of global modernity is unprecedented at this time. Some informed observers have used the phrase 'a perfect storm'[102]. They have also emphasised the urgency of the situation: the hourglass of time to act is running out.

The second is the high degree of integration of the present world system. The inherent instability pointed out by the philosopher John Gray has been noted earlier. An insight as to how collapse can occur is offered by Joseph A Tainter in *The Collapse of Complex Societies*[103]. Amongst the consequences Dr Tainter notes: "… such a quantitative decline that a dark age often ensues, population levels tend to drop and for those who are left the known world shrinks."

The third element touches on the values issue that is central to this and previous essays. The last factor that was noted in total human impact was the intangible one of values. If modernity may be read as 'values hollow' then i suggest that psychic breakdown, abetted by the material factors to which attention is commonly drawn, may be the decisive constituent of any collapse.

On the closing page of the first values essay: *Values for Our Time*[104] an extract from the Jackson Browne track *Before The Deluge* was kindly allowed reproduction.

The last four lines: -

"...and when the sand was gone and the time arrived...

...in the naked dawn only a few survived...

...and in attempts to understand a thing so simple and so huge...

...believed that they were meant to live ... after the deluge"

To cope with this it is valuable to make the switch from counting heads to counting communities. Individuals were always perishable by design. Valid cultures may have lifespans of many thousands of years.

SURVIVING VALUES

Following our third assumption – that even in the most dramatic collapse there will be some human survivors in a post-modernity[105] world – what are the implications for some of us today?

We already know that millions of people (still a small fraction of the total population) reject the values of modernity in principle, even if not in their living practice.

They are critical of the use of the Earth as a resource and dustbin. They doubt the possibility of endless growth. They can see the warning signs that others choose not to.

So what should 'we' be doing now? How should we be acting? I argue that what we should *not* be relying on are yet more exhortations that peoples and governments should change their ways 'before it is too late'.

This is to completely mis-understand both human psychology and the structural imperatives of the existing system. Drawing attention to contradictions may cause some people to think afresh – but don't hold your breath.

PLAN B

An amazing omission of both the environmental and deep ecocentric movements is that even as the calls to action become more shrill and the predictions more dire there seems to be no provision for the range of situations arising if the proposed or argued for attempts to 'turn the ship around' should fail. In other words there is no plan B. It is as if such outcomes are too horrific to contemplate.

XV. *Tsunami Wave Crashing*

Yet in each of the three possible scenarios outlined above it is the case that there will be at least some, possibly very many, human survivors trying to pick up the pieces and there will be a damaged but still ongoing biosphere to consider.

There *are* tasks to be attempted now. The first is networking: establishing bonds of mutual awareness and solidarity between all those sharing, or moving towards, Earth centred values of humility before the biosphere.

We cannot afford to remain in our silos: organisations, publications and networks with noble aims focussing on their own messages and interactions rather than the broader scene.

Movements for change are not immune from the seventh pattern of the Universe: 'every means strives to become an end'. As part of this opening up the divergents[106] amongst us, the initiators and drivers, need to watch our egos – and to be challenged. The ego-conflicts so characteristic of scientific, administrative and political establishments are an issue for us too.

There can be no doubt that a world-wide network, seriously in defence of the planet yet also anticipating traumatic futures, would be something formidable in its own right, regardless of eventual outcomes.

A second task – for us, not just for others – is closing the gap between our idealistic values and our everyday behaviours. This is where effective networks, supporting and challenging each other, do have and would have a role to play.

Since we are still talking of minorities – the recessive meme if you like – what chance that such practical idealism could survive the turmoil of social disintegration in order to be the seed values of a slow and painful recovery? All we can say is that the strong supportive networks now argued for, combined with a clear understanding of *what* was happening and also with a strong resolve that surviving ecosystems should not be further damaged by human actions ... might just come through.

AFTER THE DELUGE

What kind of post-transition world could that, should that be?

Earlier in the story reference was made to Paul Shepard, a former professor of human ecology and natural philosophy, and to his last book *Coming Home to The Pleistocene*[107].

To sum up that book's core arguments, three claims were made.

First, that our hominid ancestors evolved in the Pleistocene epoch over millions of years and Homo sapiens in particular was at home in the Pleistocene for nearly half a million years, initially as a scavenger and gatherer, only later equipped to compete with the large carnivores. During this time our bodies, our minds and our cultures evolved in tune with our environment as aware beings at ease with ourselves, capable of both co-operative and competitive modes (though for reasons of survival advantage the co-operative mode more often predominated).

Second, the emergence of agriculture and husbandry at the start of the Holocene set in train drastic and tragic consequences as explored in this and deeper essays. Paul Shepard's essential point is that we became estranged from our Pleistocene selves and from the natural world, eventually to wreak havoc on it.

The third element was a call for a return to a Pleistocene ethos, as indicated in the title. Modern nation states, mostly with the structures of priesthoods, could certainly give way to families of peoples. Yet what could the return mean in today's context and how could it be possible? It seems clear that we could not literally become those Pleistocene scavenger-hunter-gatherers again so the challenge perhaps is to return to the values that they embodied; their humility before and awe of the natural world and its ecosystems; their immanent being in the world, fulfilled in the cycles of life – even as they struggled to do what was necessary to survive.

Now if the predictions of the collapse of modernity are anywhere near the mark then one condition might already be met: low population density of scattered small communities with predominantly subsistence economies and only limited inter-trade. This community size could allow participatory decision making to become a reality.

Diets would likely be mainly but not exclusively vegetarian. The constraints in the taking of small game (say) would be both the spirit in which the 'hunt' was conducted and awareness of sufficient abundance of the prey species.

If Paul Shepard had his way agricultural production would be at the very least deprecated. This would limit available food supplies and hence population growth.

POST-TRANSITION TECHNOLOGIES

It is clear that the disintegration of complex society would lead to the passing into history of some technologies, as happened with cuneiform writing in the general collapse across the Near East towards the end of the second millennium BCE. Internet communication might be an equivalent example in this sketched future.

Large scale physical infrastructure and the technology that supported it would join the desert ruins of the great constructions of the ancient world.

XVI. *Neolithic Cave Dwellers*

Yet there would be both the motivation and the feasibility of carrying forward some modest scaled technologies, skills and wisdoms into dispersed communities, alongside re-learning others that have been lost in 'the march of progress'.

Medicine could be a prime example of this balanced approach, with some losses and gains. On the one hand the end of massive and expensive research and development programmes for bringing forward new drugs to combat (e.g.) virus infections.

On the other hand the low population densities and the demise of city living would be the most effective barrier to the spread of diseases.

Natural eating and a necessarily physical lifestyle would be further contributors to healthier active human families. Dentistry (with reduced need due to changed diets) would be a particular example of modest technology worth maintaining post transition.

In the new age of barefoot medicine the emphasis would be on treating acute ailments. Expenditure on high tech treatments for chronic conditions, often aimed at quite un-natural (in historical terms) extension of life, would simply not be available.

POST-TRANSITION SCIENCE

What role for science? With the end of the age of enlightenment and its Socratic rational optimism the great wake predicted by John Gray could commence. Wakes are ceremonies of celebration as well as mourning (if you have ever been to one). A thousand flowers can bloom. Post-enlightenment science could be one of them.

With the termination of the funding gravy train combined with the supercession of its already challenged 'universal and absolute objectivity' model, enlightenment science could retrospectively be viewed as clinging to the coat tails of enlightenment philosophy as a whole.

Now the unashamed purpose (morality) of this essay has been to challenge one of the pillars of domination of that modernity whose subjects we are. However, little credit can be claimed. If the future predictions made above are confirmed then the dis-integration (in the best sense) of modernity is assured. So to ask the question again in its new form: what role for post-enlightenment science?

The prospects could be bright. Without the economic motivations science can revert to its immanent drivers: towards understanding, appreciation and awe of our wonderful Universe, from the greatest galaxy to the tiniest flower, from the complex whole to the most basic fragments – we are part of them all.

With the declining dominance of the orthodox priesthood integrity will be the single rule. The connected and values guided science called for by Lancelot Law Whyte and others will be possible. The breach with the humanities will be healed.

Science would still retain a role it has always played: as a path finder and guide for technology. In the new situation for modest and appropriate technology.

Scientists (to the extent that some persons would continue to bear that label) would still need to eat. They would be embedded in their local communities and require the support of those communities to sometimes lift their eyes from the practical daily tasks; to acquire certain tangible aids to investigations; to transmit messages of communication with others of similar bent with whom they were endeavouring to network.

On the other side of the coin they would be able and willing to participate in local moots[108] to share new thinking, to discuss practical and ethical implications of any resulting technology and/or potential revisions of the wider world view that seemed to be called for.

A living preview in our own time of post transition science is provided by The Land Institute[109], based in Kansas US and initiated originally by Wes and Dana Jackson. A non-profit institution with enthusiastic voluntary and professional support around the world, the ethos combines a deep critique of conventional agriculture, seen as part of the project of domination of nature stretching from the agricultural revolution to modernity today ... with a very practical project to achieve viable perennial polyculture grasses and pulses (such as our Pleistocene ancestors would have gathered) as an alternative to modern monoculture.

BUT WHAT IF ...

What if the more rapid transition forecasts prove not to be correct?

From the standpoint of deep ecology the damage to the planet's network of ecosystems will continue for longer and be cumulatively greater. In terms of values struggle the contest between anthropocentric and ecocentric values would likely be protracted, with increased hostility from defenders of enlightenment orthodoxy and its fruits towards the (still) minority values of humility in partnership with nature.

What if the leading consensus among ecocentric values warriors is to stop short of the more radical implications of partnership with the biosphere, such as self-limiting human lifespans?

The basic rule of thumb is that the less effort humans are prepared to put into auto-correcting their dominance, the more will be left to the natural feedback loops of 'Gaia's revenge'[110]. This in turn implies a more passive acceptance of future human fates – a strategy that can certainly be argued for, though not by me.

Nature is amoral. Or rather it has the morality (purpose) of attempting to bring its systems (externally) to equilibrium; (internally) to maximum fulfilment in complexity.

* * * * * * * * *

REFERENCE NOTES

1.   *Values for Our Time* – Natural World Story – Patterns of The Universe – seventh pattern: *Devolve!* 2014 paperback ISBN 978 0993112607

2.   *The Social Contract*: Robert Ardrey Collins 1970 hardback ISBN 00021117908

3.   Arthur Koestler: Writer and philosopher who engaged, among other topics with the issue of mind and brain. In *The Ghost in The Machine* (1967, 1990 Penguin reprint ISBN 0140191925) he attributed much of humanity's woes to poor integration of our 'old' and 'new' brains.

4.   Paul Shepard: Professor of human ecology with wisdom to offer on human pre-history. His final book was *Coming Home to The Pleistocene* Island Press / Shearwater Books 1998 ISBN 978 1559635905

5.   Wikipedia: entry for civilisation.

6.   Friedrich Nietzsche: *The Will to Power* Re-constructions from notes of Nietzsche's last unpublished work e.g. Random House 1968 Kaufman and Hollingdale ISBN 0394704371 pp 532-533 and Penguin Classics 2017 Scarpitti and Hill ISBN 978 0141195353

7.   *Values for Our Time* – Social Story – Social Modes: - ref as 1 above.

8. *The Birth of Tragedy*: F. Nietzsche Penguin Classics 1993 ISBN 978 0140433395

9. Ibid. Sections 11 to 15 make explicit the link between the death of tragedy and the revival through Socratic optimism of the notion of an objective world beyond experience that has led us to modernity. "...Socrates used to help Euripedes with his writing. It was through their offices that the old robust Marathon soundness of body and mind was increasingly falling prey to a suspect enlightenment..." and "...spurred on by its powerful illusion, science is rushing irresistibly to its limits, where the optimism essential to logic collapses..." "...the noble gifted man, even before the mid-course of his life, inevitably reaches the peripheral boundary where he finds himself staring into the ineffable. If he sees here to his dismay how logic twists around itself and finally bites itself in the tail, there dawns a new form of knowledge, tragic knowledge..."

10. Patrick Curry, author of *Ecological Ethics* and editor in chief of *The Eco Citizen*. Article quoted from is *Defending The Humanities: Metaphor, Nature and Science* published on the DRM free site Rounded Globe. https://roundedglobe.com

11. *A New Science of Life* (Third edition): Rupert Sheldrake Icon Books 2009 ISBN 978 1848310241

12. *Deep Roots in a Time of Frost* – Essays on Tolkien: Patrick Curry Walking Tree Books 2014 ISBN 978 3905703337 Essay 5 refers.

13. *Values for Our Time* – Natural World Story – Features of The Universe – ninth feature: - ref as 1 above.

14. *Before Philosophy*: Henri Frankfort; H A Frankfort; John A Wilson; Thorkild Jacobsen Penguin Books 1971 paperback edition ISBN 014020198X

15. *The Agricultural Revolution as Environmental Catastrophe: Implications for Health and Lifestyle in The Holocene*: Clark Spencer Larsen Quaternary International 2006 volume 150, issue 1 page 12-20. Referred to by Lisi Krall in *The Economic Legacy of The Holocene*: article in *The Ecological Citizen* volume 2, issue 1 pages 67-76 ISSN 2515-1967

16. *The Paradise Papers*: Merlin Stone Virago Ltd. 1977 paperback edition ISBN 0704338076

17. Plato: Allegory of The Cave *Republic*: 514a – 520a

18. Quote from Margaret Thatcher interview in Woman's Own, 1987

19. *Values for Our Time* – Introduction – p7 + note 8 – ref as 1 above.

20. Italian scholar and philosopher, 1668 – 1774. Major work *The New Science (Scienza Nuova)* embraces most of his ideas. Critical of Cartesian rationalism.

21. *Before Philosophy*: Chapter 1, page 12 ref as 14 above.

22. *The World As Will and Idea*: Arthur Schopenhauer Everyman 1995 paperback ISBN 978 0460875059 (Sometimes translated as *The World as Will and Representation*)

23. "God does not play dice." : Brainy Quote/Albert Einstein

24. "I do not believe in the immortality of the individual … I consider ethics to be an exclusively human concern." : Brainy Quote/ Albert Einstein

25. "Because there is a law such as gravity the Universe can and will create itself from nothing." : Brainy Quote/ Stephen Hawking

26. *The Medium, The Mystic and The Physicist (Towards a General Theory of The Paranormal)*: Lawrence LeShan Turnstone Books   1974 paperback   SBN 855000384

27. *Enlightenment's Wake*: Politics and Culture at the close of The Modern Age: John Gray Routledge 1995 hardback ISBN 978 0415124751 Chapter 6: Agonistic Liberalism; Values Pluralism.

28. *Values for Our Time* – Social Story – p25 – the interface between individuality and collectivity: - ref as 1 above.

29. Phrase associated with Rousseau that occurs in Article 6 of the "Declaration of the Rights of Man and The Citizen" drawn up in the French Revolution. Intended to imply the supremacy of the collective will of all over sectional interests.

30. Fair Play: one of a number of different modes of attitude and behaviour into which both individuals and communities can 'flip' upon appropriate social triggers. *Values for Our Time* – Social Story – pp 25-27 explores: - ref as 1 above.

31. Harold Macmillan: speech on 20th July 1957: "Most of our people have never had it so good ... a state of prosperity such as we have never had in my lifetime – nor indeed in the history of this country."

32. *The Social Contract*: Robert Ardrey – Chapter 3; Order and Disorder: social strategies: - ref as 2 above.

33. *Values for Our Time* – Social Story – Social Types: - ref as 1 above.

34. Rousseau remains associated with the phrase.

35. *Leviathan*: Thomas Hobbes Oxford World Classics 1998 paperback ISBN 978 0192834980

36. Refer to 30 above.

37. *The Breakdown of Nations*: Leopold Kohr   Routledge 1986 paperback ISBN 978 0710208897

38. John Gray – article in *The Big Issue* No 863 September 7-13 2009

39. *The Ultrasocial Origin of The Anthropocene*: John M Gowdy and Lisi Krall: in Ecological Economics 95: 137-147 November 2013

40. *The Economic Legacy of The Holocene*: Lisi Krall in *The Ecological Citizen* – see ref 15 above.

41. See ref 4 above.

42. For example: *Against The Grain: A Deep History of The Earliest States*: James C Scott   Yale University Press   2018 paperback ISBN 978 0300240214   also *Agriculture and The Evolution of Human Ultrasociality*: M.Gowdy; L. Krall   Journal of Bioeconomics   volume 16 issue 2 page 179-202

43. *The Wealth of Nations*: Adam Smith (modern translation) Industrial Systems Research 2015 ISBN 978 0906321706 In this text Adam Smith introduces the metaphor of the invisible hand to describe the paradox that, though all the participants in an economy may be motivated by self-interest the total effect can be an economy thriving to the benefit of all.

44. *The Structure of Scientific Revolutions*: Thomas S. Kuhn 50th Anniversary Edition University of Chicago Press 2012 ISBN 978 0226458113

45. CNPS: www.naturalphilosophy.org

46. *History of the Unified Field Theory (UFT)*: Nexus vol. 22 No 3 April-May 2015 Part 2: Roger J. Anderton

47. *A Theory of Natural Philosophy*: R.J. Boscovitch MIT English Edition (translated by J.M. Child from the 1763 edition) 1966 ISBN 978 0262520034

48. Refer to Gregory Bateson Wikipedia article for an overview of achievements.

49. *THE FILM – An Ecology of Mind*: directed by Nora Bateson. Also Homage to Gregory Bateson by Fritjof Capra. www.anecologyofmind.com/thefilm.html and www.anecologyofmind.com/gregorybateson.html

50. "...an independent research centre exploring the frontiers of complex systems ..." www.santafe.edu

51. Kauffman's Poised Realm – Quantum Mind http://quantum-mind.co.uk/kauffman's-poised-realm/ from a review of *Re-inventing The Sacred*: Stuart A. Kauffman Basic Books 2008 ISBN 978 0465018888 Also *Humanity In A Creative Universe*: Stuart A. Kauffman OUP (USA) ISBN 978 0199390458

52. *Ingenious Genes: How Gene Regulation Networks Evolve To Control Development*: Roger Sampson MIT Press 2011 ISBN 978 0262195812

53. *The Large, The Small and The Human Mind*: Roger Penrose Cambridge University Press ISBN 978 0521785723 Contains arguments for a Quantum effect in Human consciousness developed in collaboration with Stuart Hameroff and also criticisms of their Orch-OR theory by others.

54. *Autopoiesis and Cognition: The Realisation of The Living*: Humberto R. Maturana; Francisco J. Varela D.Reidel Pub Co 1980 paperback ISBN 978 9027710161 Also *The Embodied Mind: Cognitive Structure and Human Experience*: F.J. Varela MIT Press 1992 paperback ISBN 978 0262720212

55. An in depth discussion of Heisenberg's uncertainty principle and its place in debates around Quantum Mechanics is presented on the Stanford University site: https://plato.stanford.edu/entries/qt-uncertainty/

56. *Symbiotic Planet: A New Look At Evolution*: Lynn Margulis Basic Books 1999 paperback ISBN 978 0465072729; *Acquiring Genomes: A theory of The Origins of Species*: Lynn Margulis and Dorian Sagan Perseus Books 2002 paperback ISBN 978 0465043927 For a more recent assessment: *Evolving New Organisms via Symbiosis*: E. Toby Kiers; Stuart A. West Science vol. 348 issue 6233 24th April 2015

57. *The Triple Helix: Gene, Organism and Environment*: Richard C. Lewontin   Harvard University Press 2002 paperback ISBN 978 0674006775

58. Terrence Deacon's early research included embryonic development before focusing on the human brain and mind. See ref 60 below

59. *The Essential Pierce Volume 1 (1867-1893):* Edited Nathan Houser; Christian Kloebal Indiana University Press 1992 paperback ISBN 978 0253207210   *The Essential Pierce Volume 2* (1893-1913) Pierce Edition Project   Indiana University Press   1998 paperback ISBN 978 0253211903

60. *The Symbolic Species: Co-evolution of Language and The Brain*: Terrence W. Deacon   W.W. Norton & Co 1997 paperback ISBN 978 0393317541

61. Quoted in: *Lancelot Law Whyte Unity Field Theory*: Roger J. Anderton   Proceedings of The NPA   Volume 6 No 2

62. N David Mermin: Horace White Professor of Physics Emeritus at Cornell University – theoretical physicist

63. *Theories of Knowledge and Theories of Everything*: essay by David Wolpert in *The Map And The Territory* (various contributors) Springer Science and Business Media 2018 hardback ISBN 978 3319724775

64. *The Essential David Bohm* edited Lee Nichol Routledge 2002 paperback ISBN 978 0415261746

65. *Wholeness and The Implicate Order:* David Bohm Routledge 2002 paperback ISBN 978 0415289795

66. *Commentaries On Living* (3rd Series): Jiddu Krishnamurti Ed R. Desikacharya Penguin (New Delhi) 1960 paperback ISBN 978 0144001538

67. *Fads and Fallacies In The Name of Science*: Martin Gardner Dover Publications 1957 paperback ISBN 978 0486203942

68. *The "Rediscovery" of Morphogenic Fields* in *Developmental Biology 8th Ed.* Edited by Scott F. Gilbert Sinaver Associates 2006 hardback ISBN 978 0878932504

69. *A New Science of Life* ref as 11 above.

70. *A New Science of Life* ref as above Appendix B: *Morphic Fields and The Implicate Order:* A Dialogue with David Bohm.

71. The interpretation of experimental results is currently contested.

72. *Precedence and Freedom in Quantum Physics*: Lee Smolin Cornell University Archive 2012 arXiv: 1205.3707

73. e.g. *Dogs That Know When Their Owners Are Coming Home: And other Unexplained Powers Of Animals*: Rupert Sheldrake   Crown Publishers (N.Y.) second edition 2011   ISBN 978 0307885968

74. *How The Universal Gravitational Constant Varies*: Rupert Sheldrake www.sheldrake.org/essays/how-the-universal-gravitational-constant-varies

75. Defined by Dr Patrick Curry as Techno-science, Neoliberal Economics and the Managerial State.

76. *Lancelot Law Whyte Unitary Field Theory*: ref as 61 above.

77. *Internal Factors in Evolution*: L.L. Whyte   George Braziller 1965 hardback   ISBN 978 0807602687

78. *The Next Development In Man*: L.L. Whyte Transaction Publishers (U.S.) 2002 ISBN 978 0451603999

79. *Values for Our Time*:   Natural World Story: towards an integrative science: ref as 1 above.

80. *Energy and Economic Myths*: Nicholas Georgescu-Roegan Pergamon Press 1976 paperback   ISBN 0080210562 e.g.: "To abuse a term is to use it without any attempt at explaining its meaning. In this sense 'process' has been abused in all sciences, but in none as much as in the social sciences. Most curiously, in economics the greatest abuse has taken place where one would least expect it to happen, namely, in production theory ..."

81. Terrence Deacon: Symbols   see ref 60 above.

82. *Defending the Humanities: Metaphor, Nature and Science*: ref 10 above. See page 12, para 3.

83. *Autopoiesis and Cognition: The Realisation of The Living*; also *The Embodied Mind: Cognitive Structure and Human Experience*: see ref 54 above.

84. Refer to 27 above.

85. "If I had only known I would have been a locksmith." Michael Mancur's quotations #346/ Albert Einstein

86. To give just one example: *Three Generations Left? – Human Activity and the Destruction of the Planet*: Christine Parkinson New Generation Publishing 2016 ISBN 978 1787190412

87. *Philosophy for Beginners*: Richard Osborne; Ralph Edney Writers and Readers Publishing Inc. 1992 ISBN 978 0863161575   page 99.

88. This version from the Cherokee Bird Clan: that a wise Woman of the Cree Indian Nation named 'Eyes of Fire' had a vision of the future and made the prophesy. She continued: "... mankind as we know it would all but cease to exist ... that day will come, it is not far away ... the Warriors of The Rainbow – the keepers of the legend, stories, culture and myths – would be needed

... to make the Earth green again ... that day we shall see how we owe our very existence to the people of all tribes that have maintained their culture and heritage ..."

89. *Values for Our Time* – Natural World Story: see ref 1 above   Features of The Universe – Ninth Feature – source of morality.

90. *Entropy: A Story of Science as Art*: Ashwin Vaidya PhD Assistant Professor, College of Science and Mathematics, Montclair State University. "While the traditional scientific definition of entropy is anthropocentric, and hence the common connotation of the second law is rather negative, the above metaphysical parallel of this law [from the Bhavgad Gita], if so interpreted, is devoid of this human bias and regards the return to nature as a desirable trait." https://blogs.montclair.edu/creativeresearch/2011/01/17/entropy-a-story-of-science-as-art

91. Plate XII illustrates Illich's Two Thresholds concept: a fundamental insight which has very many applications.

92. The essence of Anthropomorphism is a world view that puts humanity (including sectional interests that claim to speak for it) at the centre of the ecosphere and so justifies any values that it chooses to adopt.

93. In 1955 US retail analyst Victor Lebow summed up the approach that was now necessary: "Our enormously productive economy ... demands that we make consumption our way of life, that we convert the buying and use of goods into rituals, that we seek our spiritual satisfaction, our ego satisfaction, in consumption. We need things consumed, burned up, worn out, replaced, discarded at an ever increasing rate."

94. Quote attributed to Kenneth Boulding during hearings of the 93rd Congress of the United States on the energy reorganisation act. H.R. 11510

95. *An Essay on The Principle of Population*: T.R. Malthus Cambridge University Press 1992 hardback edition ISBN 978 0521419543 based on composite of later revised editions 1803-1826.

96. *Population versus Liberty*: Jack Parsons Pemberton Books 1971 hardback SBN 301710511

97. *The Treason of The BBC*: Jack Parsons Population Policy Press 2006 paperback ISBN 1904791050

98. Population Matters 135-137 Station Road London E4 6AG 0208 123 9116 enquiries@populationmatters.org

99. California has now joined five other U.S. States and Canada (at the time of writing) in legalising assisted dying on medical grounds. The Australian State of

Victoria has legislation in process. In Europe Holland and Belgium permit this for their own citizens only. Dignitas in Switzerland offers release for those who can afford the costs. Closer to home Dignity in Dying continues to campaign for a change in the law as well as supporting challenges in the courts by those with terminal conditions. www.dignityindying.org.uk info@dignityindying.org.uk 0207 479 7730

100. Exit International PO Box 37781 Darwin, Northern Territory 0821 Australia   www.exitinternational.net contact@exitinternational.net

101. *Damned If I Do* Autobiography: Philip Nitschke & Peter Corris Exit International

102. A former Government Chief Scientific Officer predicted in 2013 "A Perfect Storm in 30 years" if drastic action was not taken. Without using those exact words or that precise timescale others have made similar points. Most notably the 1972 MIT report to the Club of Rome *Limits to Growth*, based on computer simulations. Also worth mention is *The Growth Illusion* by Richard Douthwaite. And see ref 110 below.

103. *The Collapse of Complex Societies*: Joseph A. Tainter Cambridge University Press 1990 paperback ISBN 978 0521386739

104. Extract: Jackson Browne lyrics – 'Before the Deluge' © Kobalt Music Group Ltd.

105. Post-modernity: not to be confused with Post Modernism in social description.

106. Divergent. In *Devolve!* social theory a description for a 'leaderful' social type in a complementary relation with the Convergent type. *Values for Our Time* – Social Story – Social Types pp 28-34   ref as 1 above.

107. *Coming Home to The Pleistocene*: Paul Shepard   ref as 4 above.

108. Moot: in Anglo-Saxon England a participatory local meeting or assembly at which decisions were taken. In modern English an adjective, e.g. 'a moot point'

109. The Land Institute 2440 E Water Well Road, Salina, Kansas 67401 Visits welcome by arrangement. https://landinstitute.org

110. *The Revenge of Gaia: Why The Earth Is Fighting Back – And How We can Still Save Humanity*: James Lovelock   Penguin 2007 p'back ISBN 978 0141035352 "Despite all our efforts to retreat sustainably, we may be unable to prevent a global decline into a chaotic world ruled by brutal warlords on a devastated Earth."